MW00629316

The Quiet Escape

Inspired by actual events

Angela Moody

The Quiet Escape

Although inspired by actual events, this book is a work of fiction. Any references to historical events, real people, or real places are used fictitiously. Other names, characters, places, and events are products of the author's recollection and imagination. Names have been changed to protect those involved.

Copyright © 2021 Angela Moody
Printed in the USA
ISBN (Print Version): 978-1-7364495-0-9

All rights reserved, including the right to reproduce this book or portions thereof in any form whatsoever.

Contents

Preface

  Raised in a home with domestic violence, it was never quite clear why my mom did not leave. As a young child, I remember begging my mom multiple times to leave the situation, and she would, temporarily. In many cases, we left everything but the clothes we could carry, only to return to or be reunited with her abuser a week or so later. We left homes, towns, and even states, but the two of them always seemed to find their way back to each other.

  My brother and I were not victims of physical and verbal abuse, but we were victims.
We witnessed multiple beatings that our mom took at the hand of her abuser. We heard the verbal abuse, and we lived the constant chaos and turmoil from the environment in which we grew up around.

  We suffered embarrassment and shame for many years. Embarrassed of our parent's lifestyle, the poverty we lived in, and the shame we carried trying to explain our mother's bruised and batter face.

  After all these years, I still hold images in my mind of a tattered bag filled to the top with Barbie dolls. The Barbie legs hanging over the edge, some dressed some naked. Those dolls were the few but precious toys I could take as we packed our bags to leave, once again.

The life we lived damaged me in many ways, and I struggled with plenty of issues throughout the years due to our upbringing. Today I can say I have worked through most of those things, and I have a wonderful life to show for it. I feel blessed that we finally escaped the abuse, and I could escape from the memories that tormented me for so many years. I do not believe a lot of people do.

It is hard to understand God's plan for our lives amid our pain. I have struggled with it myself at times. Losing my dad at such a young age was devastating, especially in my teenage years and early 20's. I tried to make sense of it, only to be left with unanswered questions and emptiness I couldn't explain.

It was not until my friend read the rough draft of this book. Her words helped me understand more clearly. She said, "Angela, all your dad ever wanted was to provide for you. Even in his death, he did just that." Thinking back, I do not know what would have happened to us without the Social Security money we received after he died. That money kept us afloat and was our only source of income at times. Losing my dad was not meant to leave me empty. Losing my dad was how we survived. Even in his death, he took care of me.

I believe in healing from what has broken you; you must walk back through it and face it. Writing this book has forced me to do just that. It has been a process of healing and closure for me. My hope for this book is that the person reading it will find that same strength to walk back through their pain and face it like a warrior.

My primary purpose for writing this book is to show others what goes through a victim's mind during abuse. Why they stay, and why they go back to their abuser, how an abuser can manipulate a person so much that they question their own thoughts.

Although challenging at times, it has been a pleasure to write my mother's story, my story. After being estranged for more than ten years, my mother and I have started to rebuild our relationship.

Writing this book has helped me to see and better understand the pain my mother has been carrying for so many years. Instead of harboring resentment for the things we went through, I am just thankful we survived. She honestly did do the best she could.

Actual events from my recollection inspired this book. Timelines and stories have been modified, making this book fiction. Only a portion of the ending is true, but how I imagined things ending. The names of those involved have been changed for their protection.

Chapter 1
The Man of The House

Late September 1952. My father, Ralph, waited patiently in the hospital waiting room for my mother, Millie, to give birth to me, their first child. My father did not feel the need to be involved in the birthing process. He left that up to my mother, the doctor, and the nurses. Frankly, the thought of it made him ill.

Flipping through a Popular Mechanics magazine, he lit up one cigarette after another. Just as he began to light another, the nurse came out to announce my arrival, a healthy baby girl, and his firstborn. My father put down the magazine and cigarette and made his way to the room where my mother and I were resting. They named me Rachel.

My parents were a young couple, my father, 20, and my mother, 18, were only married a few short months when they learned of their pregnancy. It was 1952 when it was common for many young couples to marry and soon begin a family. It was also common for the men to go to work while the women stayed home to tend to their children. My mother and father were no different.

Their quiet small rural Indiana community, surrounded by cornfields and manufacturing plants, offered very few job opportunities. Manufacturing and farming were the two biggest employers. If you were not a farmer, you were likely working in one of the local factories that manufactured anything from tooling equipment to automobile parts.

Most local farms were passed down from generation to generation, making it easy to recognize a farmer by his last name. The small town was where farms had large signs proudly displayed with the family crest or family name. Your name meant everything.

Many local men joined the military after school to acquire some skills that the small community did not offer. Some graduating from high school, and others joined as early as 17 years old. The women raised babies and took care of their homes and gardens. At that time, the women wore long skirts and clothes that modestly covered their bodies. Even while they worked their gardens in the summer heat, the women stayed covered. Their hair was long, twisted in circles held by bobby pins. Few women wore makeup during those days. It was the 1950's, but that small community was always about ten years behind the times, and it showed.

My father left home at 6 am every day to work in a local factory that manufactured automobile parts. The $35 a week that he brought home was barely enough to provide for his growing family, so he picked up extra work in the spring and fall, working the fields on a neighboring farm. Exhausted, my father would come home long enough to eat dinner and grab an extra sandwich my mother made for him to take while he worked the fields, sometimes past dark.

His long-sleeve work shirt, with a patch on each side, would be covered in suet and grease from the machinery he worked with every day. The embroidered patches displayed his name on the right and the company name on the left.

Grease blackened his fingernails, and sweat streaks covered his face. Pressed for time, he would briefly sit at the dinner table to scarf down his meal. After a few short minutes, he would be out the door again.

My mother was a typical housewife, tending to the daily laundry, cleaning, and preparing meals for her family. A garden and chicken coop covered a large portion of our yard. As her family grew, so did the garden and her responsibilities.

My mother filled her days with washing cloth diapers and cooking every meal from scratch. When her garden was ready for harvesting, she would spend countless hours shucking stalks of corn, breaking beans, and canning everything she could to store food away for the winter. She gathered eggs every day, cooking some for breakfast and keeping the rest in the cellar. When the chickens quit laying, my mother cut off their heads, plucked their feathers, and prepared them for family meals. It was not a life of luxury. The hot summer days were laborsome, and she, too, was tired. During the winter months, she sewed blankets, mended clothes, and sewed buttons back on, preserving what little we had.

A few short years later, my mother found herself pregnant with their second child, my oldest baby brother. They named him Matthew. After giving birth to Matthew, mothers' duties as a housewife became even greater. She was tending to a baby and a toddler, all the while continuing with her daily workload.

Mother rarely saw my father, and she was consumed with loneliness, spending most of her time with two young children in a secluded farmhouse back a long lane.

Though the summer months brought much more work for my mother, the winter months could be harsh, stranding us at home and inside.

My father put in as many hours as he could at the local factory and on the neighboring farm, trying to keep up with his growing family costs, sometimes working 16 hours a day.

The sweltering summer heat and long days began to take their toll on him. He was searching for a way to release the stress of being a provider, husband and father. He began stopping at the local bar for a cold beer on his way home; an occasional treat for him turned into an everyday occurrence. My father began to spend more time sitting on a barstool at his favorite place than he spent at home with his family. The stale smoke smell chipped tile floors and paneled walls was where he reconnected with old friends from school and a few cousins he grew up with. It was where he released the stress of his day. Time passed quickly in that little bar as my father enjoyed the banter with old friends. We began to see less and less of him.

Arriving home late into the night reeking of beer and cigarettes, my father would crawl into his marital bed only to be met with a less than friendly welcome. My mother quickly shut down his advances, not only because of the awful stench he carried with him but because my mother herself was exhausted. She had a heavy load taking care of Matthew and me and all the household chores. She worked from sunup to sundown, seven days a week, rarely taking time for herself.

My father did not see my mother's duties as work.

Women stayed home, tended to the house and children. That was the way it was, the way it was when he grew up. My father could not understand how my mother was so tired from being home all day, and so he resented her for turning down his advances and not fulfilling her wifely duty to satisfy her husband.

My father chose to go to work at a young age instead of joining the military after seeing the effect that the war had on his older brothers. Although his family was not wealthy enough to own a farm, his father plowed fields and repaired local farmers' equipment. Watching his father and later working alongside him, my father picked up the same skills. He started by handing his father tools, and then eventually, he crawled under the tractors and repaired them himself. When having a trade was more valuable than an education, my father learned as much as possible.

Born in the early 1930s, my father grew up at the tail end of the Great Depression, a time when people relied on each other to make ends meet. When a handshake was as good as a contract, and your word meant something. He was born into a family of 13. The children were packed into beds at night or made blanket pallets in a corner to make their own. A small two-bedroom home with wood slates for floors and a wood-burning stove in the middle of the living room for heat is where my father and siblings learned most of life's lessons as they sat Indian style at the foot of their mother while she read to them every evening.

My grandfather was a smart man even though he never learned to read or write. He was quiet but had a sharp tongue, and he did not tolerate much, expecting a great deal from his wife and 13 children. Everyone had their role in the family. The boys worked the farms with their father and tended to the animals they had for their food, while the girls learned to cook, sew, clean, and raise babies. If you could walk, you had a job.

My father spent more and more of his spare time drinking with his buddies at the local tavern that sat in between a bank and a boutique on Main street, leaving my mother stranded at home all day and many nights with two little ones. If, on occasion, my mother and the wives of my father's friends were able to join in on any fun, it was at our home. The men would be seated around the table playing cards while the women tended to the children, making sure the men had endless refills of their favorite drinks and clean ashtrays. All of us children would run around like banshees, playing hide and seek and catching fireflies in mason jars. It was the only time that my mother was able to talk with other women her age, even though their conversations were usually about their husbands and children.

My mother grew up in a home similar to my father's childhood home. A packed house with nine siblings, she was taught to be a good wife and mother, learning all the essential skills at a young age. The girls were taught to obey their husbands as they are the head of the house like God is the church's head. A woman did not talk back to her husband because he knew what was best for his family. Women were expected to be submissive, reserved, and soft-spoken, quietly doing their duty as wives and mothers.

My mother was all those things, which is why my father fell in love with her. She was attractive but not beautiful, risking her running off with someone else. My grandfather once told my father to find an ugly woman; you will never have to worry about her running off with another man.

My mother was taught to be the kind of wife and mother; his mother always told him to seek. One that would be his helpmate in this world, one that would work hard, be loyal, and stand by him no matter what. That was Momma.

My father's drinking continued even in the winter months when the farming was at a standstill. He would join us for dinner, but not without a beer in his hand and a few more to follow. He sat in the same spot at the kitchen table every night, chain-smoking and drinking one beer after another. He fell out of his chair at the kitchen table many nights because he was too drunk to stand up. My mother, who was fulfilling her wifely duty, was right there to assist her husband, only to be met with his outburst of anger.

"Leave me alone, dammit. I am fine!"
"You need to go to bed, Ralph."
"I said to leave me the hell alone," my father screamed as he swatted her away.

That is how the abuse began. Night after night, my mother would attempt to get my alcoholic father to bed, and on occasion, leave him right at the kitchen table, absorbing every insult that my father in his drunken stooper could spew from his mouth.

The place where families were meant to gather was where my father continued to verbally abuse my mother.

"Why the hell did you let me sleep at the table?" My father said, raising his voice as my mother began to make him coffee and breakfast for us children.
"I tried to get you to go to bed, but you refused," my mother would meekly respond. "Here, drink some coffee; maybe you will feel better," handing my hungover father a cup of black coffee.
"You are so fucking stupid. You didn't try to do anything. You can't even get your husband to go to bed with you. How stupid are you?" My father continued to badger my mother, yelling things that made no sense.

My mother servantly served my father and us children breakfast and then sat down at the kitchen table, hanging her head as she absorbed my father's insults. As her eyes welled up with tears, she quickly wiped them, trying to keep us, but mostly my father, from seeing that she was upset. She wanted to seem stable, confident, and appear as if nothing he threw at her could break her. The strongest woman I have ever known.

"I am going to work. I can't even look at you," my father said quietly, hoping we couldn't hear him. Jumping up from her seat, my mother proudly handed him his lunch.
"Here, don't forget your lunch box."

My mother spent many days trying to understand my father's unhappiness. That was her job, after all. Or at least, she thought. It seemed nothing she did was good enough for my father. She was doing everything her mother taught her, but my father criticized her every move. Her hair was not fixed right, her clothes were unattractive, or her meals were bland.

She shrunk into a meek servant, trying to fix everything he found fault with. If her husband was not happy, it was because she was doing something wrong, and it was her job to make him happy; not doing so made her feel like a failure.

Our home was always spotless. I do not know if my mother preferred it that way or if she kept it that way, trying to prove something to my father. This particular day she cleaned it from top to bottom, prepared fresh bread for the evening dinner, knowing my father loved her fresh bread. She made sure every nook and cranny of our home was in order so he could see she was a great wife. She bathed us children and laundered my father's clothes for the next day. Exhausting herself trying to prove her worthiness, my mother did not stop. She had something to prove. She was good enough.

Shortly before my father came home from work, my mother bathed herself, dabbing on a little perfume. She fixed her hair and put on a little lipstick, although she did not wear much makeup.

My mother fixed her eyes on the clock, waiting for my father's arrival. When he did not show up at the expected time, she fed Matthew and me and tucked us into our beds.

Hearing the car pull into the driveway, she jumped up and rushed to the kitchen to prepare him a plate, knowing he would be hungry from his day at the factory.

My father stumbled into the house with his usual stench of beer and cigarettes. My mother paid no attention because she had prepared his favorite meal and had taken the time to fix herself. She was confident he would be glad to see her and indeed apologize for the night before.

My father put his lunch box on the counter and sat down in his usual spot at the dinner table. My mother put his plate in front of him, steaming hot with a fresh cold beer to wash it down. She was so proud of her day and all the things she accomplished. Sitting down to eat, my mother waited for my father to compliment the wonderful meal she prepared and maybe notice the effort she put into fixing herself.

Quietly eating, ensuring not to disturb him, my mother gently looked up from her plate to see my father staring at her. She thought to herself, he is sorry, and he is about to say so.

"What is that shit on your face?" My father said with a strange look.

"What do you mean?"

"You look like a damn whore. Have you been stepping out on me, Millie?"

"No, Ralph! I was trying to look nice for you when you got home."

"I don't believe you, you look like a whore, and you smell like a whore." Slamming his fork onto his plate, showing he was furious.

"Go wash that shit off and don't come near me, you trashy whore."

My mother slowly walked to the bathroom, hanging her head as tears began to fill her eyes. She closed the door and leaned against it, sliding down until she reached the floor, holding her face in her hands. What did I do wrong? She asked herself. She filled the sink basin with warm water and began washing her face and neck, sobbing uncontrollably. My mother spent her whole day trying to prove her worthiness, only to be reminded that she was not good enough. My father never did make her feel worthy. I watched my mother her whole life fight for the approval of that man.

My father finished his dinner and sat in the living room, listening to the radio. My mother held back tears as she cleaned the kitchen and washed the dinner dishes.

Exhausted from her day of trying to prove herself, she put on her nightgown and prepared the bed. Lying on top of the hand-stitched quilt, she had pulled back, exposing the pillow. She faced the window as tears rolled down her cheek. Admiring the full moon that lit up the entire sky, shining through the window so brightly, there was no need for a lamp. The bright night and sky full of stars reminded her of when my father took her to stargaze when they were dating. She could not figure out what went wrong, believing she was a good wife to him and mother to us children.

She did everything my father asked of her and more, so why was he so disgusted with her? Why did he make her feel as if she was not valued?

My mother and my fathers' romance began one summer night at the county fair. One of my mother's friends was dating one of my father's friends, so they introduced them.

My father was a handsome young man, tall and slender with dark thin hair. His black eyes hid behind bulky wire-framed glasses. My mother was petite, with a soft and kind personality. Her brown hair pulled away from her face revealed her unique eyes, one grey, and the other brown.

My mother never dated before, my father being the first boy who showed her any interest. She was smitten with him as he held her hand, walking around the fairgrounds, playing games as he showed off his ability to win her a giant stuffed bear. They rode the Ferris wheel, smiling from ear to ear, looking over at the county fair lights. When the fair was over, the group met at the local ice cream parlor. Again, my father held my mother's hand as they sat on a bench licking ice cream cones. Holding hands back then was a big deal. It meant you were a couple.

My father poured on the charm in the months to follow, writing love letters to my mother almost every day. He sent her poems wrapped around flowers he handpicked from his mother's flower garden. She did not care that the flowers were dead by the time they reached her, the gesture was sweet, and the flowers still had a hint of their original smell. My father told her how beautiful she was and that someday he would make her his wife.

Their courtship only lasted about six months before my father showed up at my mother's parents' home and asked for her hand in marriage. They were both excited and nervous. Back then, girls were expected to be married in their early teens; it was a blessing to my mother's parents that she would soon be leaving home.

Although my mother was only 17 years old, her parents had several other children to feed and tend to. Times were tough for their family after my grandfather lost his job and later was unable to work. My mother shared a bed with three other sisters in their overcrowded home. Leaving home meant more space for everyone else. My father seemed like a nice young man who worked hard and promised to take care of my mother, so her parents agreed to the marriage.

A month later, they were married in my father's family home, surrounded by only a few family members. My mother wore a cream-colored dress, her mother hand made from scrap material leftover from one of the babies' blankets. The ceremony lasted only minutes. After signing the marriage certificate, the young couple was off to start their life together.

My mother laid in her bed, daydreaming of a time when my father was so good to her. The sweet kindness and love that he showed, the reason she fell in love with him in the first place. At that moment, my mother promised herself to stay out of his way and do whatever he needed her to do. Be the woman her mother taught her to be, hoping he would one day see that she was a good wife and good enough. Return to being the kind man she once knew.

My mother told me different versions of that story throughout the years, even though my mother rarely shared her deepest thoughts with me. She was private and kept her feelings of sadness and loneliness to herself. She always believed that my father would someday go back to the way he was during those better times. He never did, and she spent the rest of their marriage never feeling worthy.

Women of that era were taught their feelings did not matter, take care of their men and children, and put themselves last, becoming sacrificial lambs to their families. Most of them did, passing down their teachings to their daughters, creating generations of women who never felt valuable and men who made them feel that way. I watched my mother suffer heartache, sickness, and pain alone, never receiving the comfort or companionship one seeks to have with their spouse. She was married, but she was very much alone.

I often wondered why she did not want more. Maybe she did but was unsure of what more was. As a young woman, I was certain I would never take that kind of abuse from a man. I did want more, and I knew exactly how that looked. Isn't it strange how we envision one life but end up with another?

Chapter 2
Loss of Innocence

  On this one occasion, my mother ran into an old friend
from school, Sue, at the local grocery. My mother's once a
month adventure and only time away from her home. As
simple as it seemed, it was a big day for her. She
occasionally ran into old friends or spoke to people she
encountered while shopping. It was a breath of fresh air
for my mother to see other adults and especially ones
that were not always making her feel horrible about
herself.

  Sue's mother had fallen ill with MS, and Sue struggled
to balance her own family while caring for her mother.
The two chatted for a bit in the produce section, mainly
talking about their children as we ran around the store
playing behind the displays. The two enjoyed going back
and forth, exchanging stories about what they were
doing daily and their growing children's progress,
picking up fruit and vegetables discussing the produce's
quality. After 15 minutes or so, they wrangled in us
children and continued with their shopping.

  As they said their goodbyes, Sue turned back and said,

  "Millie, do you know of anyone that might be interested
in a job sitting with my mother a couple of nights a
week? I need some help, and I am willing to pay 50 cents
an hour for someone to sit with her in the evenings.
Maybe do a few chores while they are there." Sue let out a
long sigh as she reached in her purse to grab a pen and
piece of paper.

"Here is my phone number. Call me if you think of anyone." Sue handed my mother a bit of a torn envelope with her phone number on it.

"I will ask around. I can't think of anyone, but I will let you know if I do," my mother said, reaching for the phone number.

The two parted ways and continued their shopping. My mother put the sacks of groceries in the car, strapped Matthew in the pumpkin seat, and put a seat belt around me. She started thinking about the job Sue talked about as she walked around the car, getting in the driver's seat. I could do that, my mother thought to herself. Maybe that could be the answer. Perhaps if I got a job and helped Ralph with the financial struggle, he would be kinder to me.

My mother knew she would have to work out the details, but she put some serious thought into the job opportunity. Thinking further, it seemed manageable. She could feed my father and us children, put us to bed, and go off to work, returning home before anyone woke in the morning. It was the perfect situation.

The next day my mother made a call to Sue inquiring about the details of the job. Sue was delighted that my mother was interested in the position. For many years the two had known each other, and Sue knew my mother to be a sweet, kind, and honest person.

"I would love to have you, Millie, and I am sure Mom would too. Talk it over with Ralph and call me back." Sue said before she hung up the phone.

My mother could not wait for my father to get home so she could tell him the news. She made sure we were quiet so she could focus on telling my father all the details. Dinner was on the table when my father pulled in the driveway. Today he was on time and had not been drinking, which was a wonderful surprise and rarely happened.

"How was your day, dear?" Shooting a glance at my father.
"I am tired. What's for dinner?"
"I made a meatloaf, using your mother's recipe." Smiling with confidence.
"That sounds good. I love my mother's meatloaf." Waiting to be served, my father turned to wink at my mother. There he is, she thought. That kind, gentle and sweet man I fell in love with so many years ago.
My father seemed to be pleased with the meatloaf, even thanking my mother for the delicious dinner. Something he hadn't done in a long time, but he hadn't been sober for a long time either. Pleased by my father's reaction to his dinner, my mother got up enough courage to start the conversation about the job opportunity.

"I saw Sue from school today at the grocery." My mother said, striking up a conversation.
"That's nice."
"Did you know her mom has MS, and she is taking care of her?"
"No, I didn't. That's too bad."

"She is looking for someone to help her a couple of nights a week, sitting with her mother. I thought maybe I could do it." My mother slouched her shoulders and hung her head waiting for my father's reply.

"How do you think you can do that, Millie? You have a family here to take care of. You can't be going out every night, leaving the children and me alone." He glanced sternly at her.

"I have it planned out. I will be here for dinner and to put the kids to bed. Once they are asleep, I will go to Sue's mother's home for a few hours. I will be home before anyone wakes up in the morning." Barely stopping to take a breath, my mother continued with her plan.

"Rachel will be going to school soon, and I can take a nap with Matthew if I get tired during the day. Don't worry, Ralph; you won't even know I am gone. It pays 50 cents an hour, Ralph; we could use the extra money."

A few minutes pass, never looking up from their plates, the two continued to eat their dinner.

"I guess it would be okay, but the first time you can't fulfill your duties here, you will quit. You understand me?" My father pointed his fork at my mother, giving her his I mean it look.

They finished eating, and like always, my mother cleaned up the dinner dishes while my father listened to the news on the radio in the living room. As soon as my mother finished her chores, she called Sue to tell her that my father agreed she could take the position.

"When can I start?" My mother said to Sue with excitement.

"Ralph said I could take the job, so when can I start?"

18

"Tomorrow, can you start tomorrow?" Sue was thrilled and relieved.

"I will be there at 9 pm," my mother excitedly said, almost shouting before she hung up the phone.

My mother planned the following day perfectly. My father would not be bothered by her absence, and the extra $9 a week would make a big difference for their growing family. Once everyone was off to bed, my mother clutched her pocketbook under her arm and drove the short 3 miles to Sue's mother's home. My mother would stay for 6 hours, three nights a week, so Sue could go home and sleep in her bed. It was a perfect fit. Sue got a break, and so did my mother. She was good at it too. Taking care of others is what my mother did best. She felt fulfilled.

My father did not mind that my mother had a job as long as he didn't have to pay much attention to Matthew and me. He worked and brought home a paycheck; everything else was my mother's responsibility. He was not the kind of father who would read children's stories before bed or take us to the park and push us in a swing. A cold shell of a man, our father, was nothing more than the provider.

My father believed children were to be seen and not heard and did not serve much of a purpose until they were older and could help work, doing chores around the home. Though she rarely did, my mother made threats about having our father deal with us when he returned home. We were terrified of him, and rightfully so.

Our father did not offer much affection to us, or our mother, for that matter. All we saw was him coming home drunk, tirelessly screaming obscenities at our mother, demanding she meets his every need. We did not revere our father; we only saw him as a bully and a drunk. I cannot recall a time when I saw him sober. We were a family, but not an affectionate or loving one, never exchanging hugs and kisses or I love yous. Maybe all families were like that back then, but I don't think so. As we grew older, I was around five and Matthew three, our father would occasionally smack us on the back of the head as we passed by. That was the extent of the affection he showed.

"Go outside and play, you little bastards. I am tired of looking at you." He would slur with a cigarette hanging from his mouth and a beer in his hand.

Our mother scurried around, hushing us, trying to keep us away from his grip. We did not play inside when our father was home because he preferred it to be quiet so he could listen to a ballgame or read the newspaper. His cold and stale aura darkened every room he entered. We instinctively coward in his presence, keeping our distance, and staying out of his way. Our mother endured years of insults and abuse from our father. Though she never made it seem as if it was wrong, only deserving. We knew nothing different.

Fall was a beautiful time in Indiana. The vibrant colors of the changing leaves could leave you breathless. Some farms and even streets looked like painted pictures; that is how unbelievably beautiful they were. The beauty of the orange, red, and yellow leaves did not last long, and it was a grim reminder of what was to come. Winters could be brutal with the snow, ice, and hollowing winds. The grey and gloomy days seemed to last forever.

Although the accumulating snow brought some enjoyment outside, we knew that we would be stuck in the house under our fathers' thumb for those few months, a dreadful time.

As winter set in, our old brick farmhouse stayed cold and drafty. The home was large with tall old windows and exposed brick in some of the rooms. The old house was not well insulated, and there was a constant chill from the air blowing in through the cracks under the doors and gaps around the windows. We used old newspapers to fill in the gaps the best we could, but the old furnace that emitted a fuel oil smell through the registers every time it kicked on could not keep up, and we didn't have the money to fix it. It seemed there were not enough blankets to keep us warm, closing off unused rooms.

One of those cold winter nights in that old brick house is when the real terror began for me. Once my mother left for work, my father entered my bedroom, scooped my five-year-old body up from my bed, and carried me into his. Wearing a long nightgown with pink bunnies and bows, my body stayed limp as my head hung off my father's arm.

Startled and barely awake, I looked up to see my father holding me.

"It's okay; you are going to sleep with Daddy tonight so you can stay warm," my father said softly, looking down with a smile.

At first, I met this with such delight. My father never paid much attention to me, let alone act as if he cared about my wellbeing. I felt special, and the extra warmth was pleasant. I slept for a few hours as my father wrapped himself around my little body, keeping me warm. Carrying me back to my bedroom shortly before my mother was to arrive home, my father cradled me in his arms as he whispered:

"Don't you tell anyone; they will get jealous and be mad at you." I shook my head in acknowledgment.

This same ritual went on for several weeks. On the three nights a week, my mother was away, my father repeatedly picked me up from my bed and put me in his, returning me before my mother arrived home. I did not speak a word of it to anyone. I feared my father even though it seemed as if he was showing a gentler side of himself. A side that I rarely saw.
Darkness fell as early as 5 pm on those winter evenings. The hallowing winds blew snow as it began to accumulate on the ground, blowing it into drifts on the roads and up against the house.
On the coldest and darkest night of the year, the snow had been coming down most of the day, causing the roads to be nearly un-drivable.

My father stayed up, assuring my mother made it safely to Sue's mother's home, drinking beer, and listening to a ball game. Once my mother called telling him of her arrival, my father scooped me up from my bed and laid me beside him in his just like he had done many nights before.

  The cold crisp sheets startled me as my father placed me in the same spot, my mother's side of the bed. Looking up with relief, I was happy for the extra warmth. It was cold, and we were all struggling to stay warm. I rolled over, snuggling into the blankets, trying to get comfortable so I could fall back to sleep. I jumped as I felt my father's cold hand inch its way between my legs. I pushed his hand as if he were unknowingly touching me in the wrong place, but my father only met me with more force.

  "Quiet!" My father whispered loudly. "All daddy's do this. Just stay still."

  My father began to rub my private area with a few fingers and then slowly moving his hand across my chest and then back down into my panties. A fierce wind outside his bedroom window and the trees beating against the house muffled the sound of my crying. I scanned the room, searching for anything to focus on, keeping me from looking at his dark beady eyes. I locked my eyes on the antique rocking chair sitting by the window. The same chair my mother rocked me in as an infant, humming old church hymns until I fell asleep.

Tears rolled down my face as I laid there frozen in fear. I did not know what to do. I was only five years old. He was my father, the one man I was supposed to look up to and trust. The man that was supposed to protect me from this cruel world. Instead, he was touching me in this inappropriate way. What is happening? I thought.

My father continued fondling me for hours until he tired and fell asleep. Like clockwork, he picked me up and put me back into my bed before my mother returned home. This time he kissed me on the forehead before laying me down. My father never kissed me. I never saw him kiss my mother. That type of affection was non-existent in our home.

I was terrified and barely slept with the constant touching from him, too young to understand what was happening and why it was happening. I felt gross, dirty, and unsure of the situation, but I finally cried myself to sleep. I went to school the next morning as if the incident never occurred. Perhaps it was a dream; maybe it did not happen. I kept quiet, not knowing if my mind was playing tricks on me.

My mother's new job seemed to be working out just fine. We were all settled into the new routine, and my father did not seem to be bothered by my mothers' absence three nights a week. My mother had no idea what was going on in her home while she was gone those six hours. She did not know that my father had found something new to occupy his time, his daughter.

My mother believed her plan had worked out beautifully. It was the first time in her marriage that she had enough money to visit a beauty salon and get her hair done.

She was feeling better about her marriage and confident about herself. Even my father was more pleasant to her when they did see one another. To my mother, everything was falling into place.

My father molested me for several years. It became more intense and more forceful the more he drank and the older I became. Three nights a week, my father carried me to his room, having his way with me as I laid lifeless. For hours he fondled my little body, barely older than a toddler. The molestation turned into rape as my father began penetrating me, pinning me down as he forced himself on top of me. He would put the head of his penis inside me, just enough for him to get aroused so he could finish as he sat on the side of the bed.

"Did you like that?" My father would say as he cleaned himself with a towel from the hall closet.

I would lay there staring at the ceiling, not knowing what to do. Like what? Is this supposed to be fun? I would think to myself. The pain and the trauma from my father's abuse paralyzed me, confused me, and left me unsure about everything. In the evenings, my father treated me as if I were a grown woman who should enjoy his company and the affection he was showing me, but during the day, I was the little girl that should be seen and not heard, who should play outside and stay out of his way.

This confusing attention was the only love or affection my father ever showed me. The disgusting sexual acts that he performed on me or made me perform on him was the only relationship I had with my father. Do all fathers do this? I thought.

25

As I got older, my father stopped picking me up out of my bed; instead, he would summons me to his room on the nights my mother worked. I would hang my head in shame as I walked to my father's room three nights a week. Resembling a death row inmate on the way to the gas chamber. My lips would begin to quiver; I knew the fate of every time my father called for me. There was nothing I could do. If I refused, he would whip me with his belt and still force me into his room. Tormented, I clammed up and became numb, bracing myself each time I made that dreaded walk down the hall.

My father continued the abuse during the day when my mother ran errands or visited friends. Grabbing me by the hair, demanding I perform oral sex on him or touch his penis, taking every opportunity to be alone with me so he could trap me in a closet or corner, forcing himself onto me.

My father threatened me to stay quiet, even insinuating it was my fault. Not only was my father sexually abusing me, but he was emotionally abusing me too. Isolated in that old farmhouse, I had no friends and no escape. I wanted to run, but where would I go? Who would believe me? I was just a child, and children have wild imaginations.

"Stop your crying. You know you enjoy it, or you wouldn't come in here every night. You are just as guilty as me, and if you say anything to anyone, I will tell them that you wanted it." My father told me repeatedly.

Believing all my father's threats, thinking he would tell everyone that his little girl was throwing herself at him. I was too afraid to utter a word about what was going on. All I knew was my father would make people mad at me and somehow make it my fault. I began to feel guilty for the horrible acts my father was forcing on me. I started blaming myself, but I did not know how to stop it. I couldn't stop it. My father's mind manipulation was working.

My mother kept her job taking care of Sue's mother for four more years until she discovered she was pregnant with my second baby brother. For those five years, I was subjected to sexual abuse from my father three nights a week and occasionally throughout the day.

I suffered silently.

I was filled with excitement when I heard the news of my mother's pregnancy. I knew if my mother was home, my father could not continue to abuse me. Even though he found ways to be alone with me when my mother was gone, I knew the nightly abuse would stop. My father, however, was furious.

"How in the hell did you get pregnant?" My father yelled when my mother told him the news.

"What are we going to do with another mouth to feed and one less income? How could you let this happen, Millie?"

"I didn't do this by myself, Ralph."

"Don't you backtalk me," my father said as he hit my mother with the backside of his hand. My mother grabbed her face and began to sob.

27

"Get away from me; I can't stand the sight of you. You probably got pregnant on purpose so that you could get sympathy. You are so pathetic."

When my mother reached six months pregnant, she broke the news to Sue that she would have to quit her job to take care of their soon to be infant son. By this time, I was ten years old, in school, and developing into a young woman. I was looking forward to the new little brother and the break from my fathers' abuse. I helped my mother as much as I could, preparing bottles, and doing chores around the house. I was keeping busy trying to still the voices in my head. The voices that told me how dirty and awful a person I was. That I would never be worthy of someone's love because my father had taken the one thing that every girl cherishes, her virginity.

My mother never spoke to me about sex, only spelling it out "S. E. X." when talking with other adults in my presence. It was taboo in those days. Even adults did not speak openly about sex unless they were hookers or the men seeking them. What little I knew I learned from school and my father. My mother was naive to the fact that I knew a great deal about sex before I could write my name. I did not know everything, but I did know that everyone thought a woman who had sex before marriage was a whore. So, I must be a whore. My father always reminded me of it too. Suggesting that I was nothing more than a worthless whore.

I AM A CHILD!
I wanted to scream at him so many times, but fear always stopped me. I didn't want to be a whore; I didn't even know what it meant. I didn't do this. He did, but somehow it was my fault. It was like because I existed, I turned him into this sexual predator. I did not ask to be here; I don't want to be here; I thought.

"God, please get me out of this place. If you are real, God, why are you letting this happen to me?"

I stayed close to my mother's side, mostly when my father was home. At this point, I was old enough to know that the things my father had been doing to me all these years were wrong, avoiding him as much as I could. My father's nightly sexual abuse stopped with my mother returning home in the evenings, but the physical abuse got worse. His drunken outbursts turned into him, whaling his belt at us children for the smallest things. A small sigh or a toy left out would get us a beating. The leather whistled as my father unbuckled his belt, sliding it through the hoops of his pants. He would swing his belt as hard as he could at Matthew and me, hitting us anywhere and everywhere. If we tried to run, he would grab us by the head of the hair holding us in place while he swung his belt as hard as he could. He would not stop until he was tired. My father considered this discipline, but it was abuse.
My mother could not do anything to stop the abuse. She was just as scared as us children because she, too, was a victim of my father's. The verbal abuse intensified and he began to abuse her sexually.

If my mother refused his advances, he would force himself on her, holding her down while he had his way. He would ejaculated on her face, laughing as she closed her eyes and cried. My father saw this as a form of birth control and punishment for refusing him. As if it was all my mother's fault that she got pregnant three times. All my mother knew how to do was to take care of her husband. She was horrified by his actions, but she believed it was her job to do whatever her husband wanted, submit.

We were all terrified of my father even though we began to see him as a worthless drunkard. His eyes had turned black and beady, the blood vessels around his nose began to show through his thin pale skin, all the signs of alcoholism. My father's eyes showed the evil inside of him, the window to the soul. We did not respect our father; we only feared him. My mother did not have that same love and affection for him that she once did, but she saw no way out. We all felt trapped.

Trapped in a life of fear and abuse, I developed nervous tendencies, wetting the bed into my teens. Matthew had a sleep disorder that caused him to sleep for days. My mother just hunkered down, trying to steer clear of my father. The abuse continued, but as Matthew and I became teenagers, we spent less time at home. We were taking every opportunity to stay at a friend's house for the night or attend a ball game or dance that would last longer than our father could stay awake.

Matthew spent much of his time playing baseball, spending hours on the field practicing, or away playing against other teams in our conference.

Matthew was good looking and a great athlete. He had no trouble finding friends or girls to spend his time with, keeping him away from home and eventually causing him to get his girlfriend pregnant at 15 years old.

I began to find solace at my cousin's home, where it was peaceful. I was not in fear of being touched or beaten when I was there. My aunt would plan nights baking cookies, telling stories, and fixing each other's hair and makeup. I would even spend entire months during the summer there, a much-needed break. My cousin was a few years older than me, but we were close, even best friends.

One thing I could not shake was my constant nervous bladder causing me to pee the bed. My aunt would be so upset with me, having to change the sheets for the first night or two that I stayed. She would put plastic down under the sheets on the already uncomfortable bed so that I wouldn't soil the mattress. I was embarrassed, but I couldn't control it.

Only when I settled in did it stop, usually after a few nights away from home. This problem prevented me from staying with many of my friends. No one wanted someone peeing in their bed. My aunt was the only one who did not seem to be too bothered by it. She would be frustrated, but she would always help me clean up, and she never made me feel bad about it. She never told the others about it either, embarrassing me further. She was like a second mother to me, and I needed that in my life.

One evening my cousin was gone, staying with a friend from school. It was just my aunt and me hanging out, enjoying snacks, and watching television. It was then that I finally broke the silence, telling my aunt about the years of sexual abuse from my father. We sat at the kitchen table sipping coffee, crying as I poured my heart out and finally told the secret I had been keeping for so long.

"We need to tell your mother, Rachel." My aunt said as she held back tears.
"I don't think I can tell her," I replied.
"I will help you. When your mother picks you up next week, we will tell her together. Okay?"
"Okay." I shook my head.

I was so relieved to finally tell someone about the horrors I had been going through. I trusted my aunt. I knew she cared about me, and I just knew that she would find a way to get me out of that house for good. The following week, I became anxious, anticipating the conversation I was going to have with my mother. What would she say? How would she act hearing the news of the abuse? Did she know? I did not know what to expect. I was nervous but relieved, imagining we would leave my father after telling my mother everything he had done. The day finally came, and as my mother went into the house, I met her at the door.

"Come sit down, Mother; I need to talk to you," I said softly.
"Are you pregnant?"

"No, Mother, I am not pregnant, but this is a serious conversation," I said as I pulled out a chair for her to sit down.

My aunt sent her daughter outside with the other children as not to be disturbed when we told my mother what happened to me over several years. My voice began to crack as I told her about the sexual abuse from my father. I slowly spoke, swallowing, trying to clear the thump in my throat. I was finally letting it all out. A sense of shock came over my mother's face as she began to cry.

"How could this happen? Oh my God, how could this happen?" My mother blubbered as she started crying.

"What am I supposed to do? I have three children at home and no job. If we leave, where will we go?" My mother continued.

"Rachel, let me talk to your mother alone. Go outside with the other kids. Your mother will come to get you when we finish talking. It will be okay, sweetie." My aunt explained as she touched my arm, reassuring me.

"Millie, I am your sister, and I am going to tell you what you need to do. You are going to go home and confront that son of a bitch, pack you and the kids some clothes, and come right back here. Tomorrow you will go to the bank and draw out every penny in your account. Then you are going to contact someone that can help Rachel work through this. Do you understand me?"

"How do I know this is true? What if Rachel is making it up because she hates her father so much? What then?"

"Rachel isn't making this up, Millie. She is a child." My aunt leaned in closer to my mother, grabbing her hand.

My mother sat quietly with her face in her hands.

"I need to get home. The kids are probably hungry." My mother pushed in her chair, hanging her head in shame.

No one spoke a word during the car ride home. My mother avoided eye contact with me for the next few days, and she never got enough courage to confront my father or talk to me about the abuse. She was at a loss for words, so she just went on about her daily routine. My mother laid in bed many nights, running scenario after scenario over in her mind. Was it her fault? Did she neglect her husband so much that he felt a sexual desire for his daughter? Did I make advances at my father for attention? All these things kept running through my mother's mind, along with wondering how she would make it without my father's financial support.

The only solution my mother could come up with was to ignore what happened if it happened. It had been several years since the abuse so just make sure my father was never alone with me ever again. Go on with life, and hope that I would someday forget. Fix it the only way she knew how. Sweep it under the rug, forget about it and move on.

In all the years since the abuse, I have never told my mother everything or the full details. I know it would be hard for her to hear, and I was and still am too ashamed and embarrassed to even speak about some of the horrible things my father did to me.

Chapter 3
Runaway

I never forgot.

The abuse from my father and my mother's denial started me on a path of destruction and a life of abuse. As a teenager, I began to rebel. I was smoking cigarettes that I stole from my father, attending parties, staying out all night, and drinking. I started to steal clothes and makeup from the local department stores. We were poor, but I was popular, a cheerleader, and wanted to have the same things as my friends. I tried my best to appear as if I had a normal life. My rebellion was more of a cry for help. I was not a bad kid, but I thought that someone would ask me why I was doing these things if I did enough bad things. Someone would care enough to want to help me, and then I could tell them. Maybe they could take me away.

Eventually, the stealing became a high for me, a sense of satisfaction that I could get away with something. Hiding what I stole from my parents or telling them I borrowed the things from my friends. My mother tried to keep my rebellion away from my father. She felt an extreme amount of guilt for never confronting him, and she feared he would put a severe beating on me for the things I was doing.

My mother tried to manage the punishment the best she could by taking privileges away from me, but it seemed nothing was working, mainly because my rebellion was not the real problem.

She found herself always covering for me, to only later scolding me when my father was not around. At this point, I had the upper hand, and I knew it. In a way, I was purposely showing my mother that I was in charge.

I felt betrayed by her for not speaking out, confronting my father, and standing up for me. I could not understand how my mother could lay beside a man every night knowing what he did to his daughter, her daughter. I knew I was taking a risk if my father found out, but I wanted my mother to see that I had not forgotten. I wanted her to know what affect her betrayal and my father's abuse had on me. If she were not going to help me, I would punish her in my way.

One evening my mother and father sat at the dinner table with the boys when there was a knock at the door. I was supposed to be at my cousins for the weekend, but there I was with a police officer standing behind me.

"Ma'am, your daughter, Rachel, was caught stealing these blouses." The police officer held up two blouses as he firmly had a hold of my arm.

"You will need to pay $6.50 to the department store, or they are going to have your daughter arrested." My mother had no time to think before my father entered the room.

"What the hell is this?" My father said, pointing at me. The police officer repeated himself to my father, explaining the situation. My mother quickly grabbed her pocketbook and pulled out $6.50, and handed it to the officer.

"Thank you, ma'am. I suggest you teach this young lady a lesson." The officer tipped his hat and turned to leave.

As soon as the door slammed shut, my father grabbed me by the arm as he loosened his belt. I could hear the whistling sound from the leather moving through his belt loops as I braced myself and then began to cry. I knew what I was in for, a beating I would never forget. This time my mother could not hide what I had done. I embarrassed them. A cop car pulled into the driveway with their daughter being led out by a police officer. What would the neighbors think?

"Mom, Mom stop him," I cried out.

My mother turned her head as my father began to whale his belt at me. The belt slipped from his hand, the buckle catching the backside of my legs. He swung it harder and harder, knocking over anything that got in his way. My mother could see welts form on my legs, one on top of another, as she peeked through her fingers, covering her eyes with her hands.

"Ralph, that's enough. That's enough."

My father was out of breath from exerting so much energy, as he turned to my mother, slumped over gasping for air.
"You shut your damn mouth, or you are next. I have had enough of the both of you." Snapping his belt in my mother's direction. He let go of my arm as I fell to the floor. My mother rushed over to me, trying to console me as we both cried.
"Come on, honey; I will run you a bath." She whispered as she pulled me to my feet.

My mother treated my wounds and kept me from school for a few days so that no one could see the damage. Once the welts faded, she sent me back to school, and life went on as usual, whatever that was for us.

I was more determined than ever to get out of my parent's home after the severe beating my father just gave me. I wanted away from his abuse once and for all and did not care how I did it. I hated him. I hated him for the sexual abuse and physical abuse he inflicted on me. I hated him for existing. I was supposed to love this man, but I despised everything about him.

I began to contemplate my exit plan. I was looking for any opportunity to free myself from that place. I couldn't even call it home. A home is where you find solace and comfort. That place, that house was hell for me.

I knew a few older guys from school that had an apartment. I had been there for parties a few times, and I thought maybe I would ask them to let me move in and help out. I figured I could get a job, help clean and do their laundry. I wanted out no matter what I had to do. Even if I had to wash their stinky socks by hand, it had to be better.

One weekend I told my mother I was going to my cousins, but instead, I ended up at that apartment, and I intended not to leave. I had run away from home; just no one knew it yet. I asked to stay after I cleaned up and showed the guys that I could be a good roommate. They needed a women's touch; it was a typical bachelor pad.

As the evening started, several people were arriving for the usual weekend party. On the couch sat a stocky strawberry blonde young man with piercing blue eyes.

He kept looking at me as I picked up cups and emptied ashtrays. I was a beautiful young girl back then with long dark hair and flawless skin. I was well-liked, and I had a smile that could light up a room. Others had told me.

I noticed the young man staring at me, but I continued to look away as I cleaned up everyone's messes. I knew I had a reason for being there. I was not trying to meet anyone. Making eye contact with me, the young man motioned for me to come over and sit down.

Reluctantly I smiled and moved toward the sofa where he was sitting surrounded by half-empty cups and empty beer bottles.

"I am Chance; what's your name?" He said with a friendly smile.

"My name is Rachel," I responded softly.

"Why don't you come to sit down for a few?" Chance pats his hand on the sofa. "You have been working hard. Come take a break."

I complied and sat with Chance, watching other people come and go as we chit-chatted and got to know each other. My friends agreed to let me stay at the apartment for the next few nights. Chance stayed with me, and we stayed up all night talking about our childhoods and the dreams we had for our futures.

I thought Chance was sweet and charming. He confided in me about the abuse he received from his father too. It seemed as if we had a connection, an immediate bond. I told Chance about my plan to talk to my friends about staying there and getting a job.

I knew I could not go home, and I did not want to go home. By now, my parents surely knew I ran away, and going back would result in another beating like the one I received a few weeks prior.

I was only 17 and a senior in High School. Chance was 18 and just graduated with plans to join the Marines. We were both young with big dreams. I wanted to be a flight attendant and fly all over the world, experiencing everything I could. However, that dream would never come true for me.

I thought the military sounded adventurous, and I could see myself having a life with Chance. Any life away from my father had to be better. Maybe military life could fulfill my dreams to travel and see new things. I could get away from the small Midwest town and as far away from my father as I could. Chance and I continued to stay at the apartment for the next week, bonding and getting to know each other. We laughed and enjoyed each other's company. He was fun and a bit wild, but I found that exciting.

I did not know if I could be loved, loved in the way that I always dreamed of. I didn't even know if that kind of love existed. My father never loved my mother that way, and he surely didn't love me that way. The abuse I took from my father and the denial from my mother shattered me on the inside. The only love I knew was dysfunctional. I didn't even love myself, so how could someone else love me?

Chance did not want to go home either. He was the baby of 4 children; even though it was less than what his siblings endured, Chance was subjected to his father's violence and stepmother's neglect.

When his mother passed away from breast cancer, he was only five years old, so his older siblings played a big part in raising him and protecting him. His father re-married shortly after his mother's passing, looking for someone to help raise his four children. His stepmother was less than nurturing and was downright mean. Chance rarely spoke about his childhood, only that he had an incredible yearning for his mother, whose life was taken too soon.

"Why don't we get married?" Chance said, grinning at me.

"Are you crazy? We barely know each other," I responded with a smirk.

"We will get to know each other." Chance persisted.

"I am only 17," rolling my eyes at Chance.

"I will tell your parents about my plans for the Marines. Surely, they will be excited about that. People our age get married all the time." Chance went on as he tried to convince me.

"Okay, I will marry you as long as I never have to go back to that house again. I am never going back there. So, is this a proposal?"

"I guess it is. Is that a yes?" Chance grabs my hand.

"Yes, I will marry you. Let's do it. Why not?"

We discussed our plans a little more for a few days. We laughed at how we only knew each other a couple of weeks and would soon be married.

Chance was trying to get up the courage to ask my father for my hand in marriage, and he was a little intimidated, knowing the stories I told about my father.

41

Chance left me at our friend's apartment while he headed home to round up all the money he had saved over the years and to sell a few things of value. He wanted to do the right thing by renting an apartment and buying me a ring. He was a hard worker, and he had been working extra hours at a factory trying to save money for a fancy car he always dreamed of owning. He never thought he would be using that money to buy a ring instead. Chance did not seem to mind, though. He thought I was the prettiest girl he ever laid eyes on, and now I was going to be his wife. We were both so wrapped up in the thought of having our own lives and getting away from our childhood homes that we thought nothing about what being married consisted of.

Chance bought me a modest ring that he gave me with a "will you marry me?" proposal at our friend's apartment. Shortly after, we drove to my parent's home that I had been absent from for the last few weeks, so that he could ask my father for my hand in marriage. As I open the front door, the two boys came running towards me.

"Where have you been?" Asks Matthew.

"I was taking a break," I replied.

My mother came around the corner from the kitchen, wiping her hands on a dishtowel.

"Oh my God, Rachel. Where have you been? I have been worried sick over you."

"Momma, this is Chance, my fiancé. Where is Daddy? Chance wants to talk to him." I asked.

"Your Daddy is really sorry, Rachel." My mother says, fearing Chance was there to do him harm.

"Chance wants to marry me, Momma."

"Marry you? You are only 17, and you haven't even graduated yet." My mother says with concern.

"Momma, he's going to be a Marine, and he is going to take care of me. Plus, you and Daddy were married at our age." I pleaded.

"Go talk to your father. He is out in the garage." My mother sighs.

Chance and I walked across the yard to the garage, holding hands, trying not to look nervous.

"Dad!" I called out.

"Well, look what the cat dragged in." My father turns from his workbench with a cigarette hanging from his mouth. "Where the hell have you been? And who the hell is this?" He asks, wiping motor oil from his hands.

"My name is Chance, sir. I want to marry your daughter." Chance extends his hand to shake my fathers.

"So, marry her, I don't give a damn. She is nothing but trouble." My father turned toward the workbench, wiping down his wrenches, never extending his hand to Chance.

"Sir, we need your written consent since she is only 17." Chance slowly walks over to my father.

"Have her mother do it. I don't have time for this nonsense. Now go on."

"Okay, sir, thank you, sir." Chance says as he tries to extend his hand again for my father to shake.

Chance and I went back inside to tell my mother that my father said it was okay for us to get married. We gave my mother a few details before heading home to our new one-bedroom apartment Chance rented for us.

43

I felt guilty leaving my mother and two brothers in that house. My brothers and I comforted each other many times throughout the years, especially my second brother. He was very special to me; I practically helped raise him to that point. He always wanted to be with me. He was a special little boy and very special to me. I did not want to leave either of them, but I knew I couldn't stay. Soon they would both be old enough to go on their own. I was getting out, and this may have been my only chance.

Chapter 4
The First

It was a scorching hot September day, 1969, when we married in Chance's brother's living room. I wore an old winter ball dress from high school, and Chance borrowed a suit from his brother. Just as he promised, Chance signed up for the Marines and only had a couple of weeks before he was gone for 13 weeks of basic training, so the two of us honeymooned in our little apartment, eating grilled cheese sandwiches and tomato soup.

Before I knew it, Chance was gone and would not be back for a long time. I made the most of our little one-bedroom, upstairs apartment. The walls were bare, and the furniture was sparse, but it was ours, and I was away from my father for good. My mother would stop by often to check on me, bringing me little things to decorate with and a few groceries here and there.

Since Chance was married, he could use the phone more frequently, but the long-distance phone calls were expensive, so we had to keep them short, calling only once or twice a week. If he couldn't call, he would try to write at least once a week to keep the communication between us open. Only knowing each other a few short weeks before getting married meant we were learning each other through letters and brief phone calls, like pen-pals.

I was getting lonely since I dropped out of high school. I was married now, and my friends were less inclined to call to invite me to dances or high school parties.

I also began to feel ill a few weeks after Chance left, keeping me from seeing any friends or going to many places. Hearing of my sickness, my mother came by one morning and took me to the doctor since I did not have a vehicle at the time. A test showed I was pregnant.

I could not wait to tell Chance the next time he called; I knew he would be excited. I waited and waited for his call, but two weeks had passed, and I had not heard from him. Concerned, I checked the mail daily and sat by the phone when I finally received a letter explaining why he could not call me.

Chance had been in several fights with other service members, mostly Army men off base. He had his phone privileges taken away along with other rights because of his constant drinking and fighting. He was in trouble, but I was paying for it too. All I wanted was a little conversation with my husband. That exciting feeling I had about being with a bad boy didn't seem so exciting anymore, especially when I was alone most of the time and now pregnant.

Finally, Chance called.

"I have five minutes, sweetheart, five minutes." Chance said quickly.

"Chance, we are having a baby, I shouted with excitement. I'm pregnant."

"Really? Is it true? Boys, I'm going to be a daddy." Chance yells at the other men standing in line for the payphone.

I could hear all the men cheering and whistling in the background like they just won the World Series.

"I have to go, sweetheart. I am crazy excited about the baby. I will call again soon." The phone went dead as I held the receiver in my hand for a few minutes listening to the dial tone.

That was it, the only conversation I had with my husband in over three weeks and maybe the only conversation I would have for another few weeks. I was lonely.

Chance's 13 weeks of basic training turned into 26 weeks. He was a stocky young man (a fat body; they called them in the military) and failed to lose an adequate amount of weight. The Marines sent him back to basic training for a second go-around, ensuring he would be in a lean condition.

Chance was able to come home for a few days after graduating from his 26 weeks of training but shortly had to return for his specialized training.

His specialized training would last for another eight weeks before he would know of his permanent location. I waited for over an hour at the bus stop, anticipating his arrival. I barely recognized him when he stepped off that Greyhound bus. He was a hundred pounds lighter and muscular. He was in lean condition, but here I was, pregnant and fatter than a house. Nothing had changed about those piercing blue eyes, though. They looked like clear blue ocean water and somehow made you feel as if they could see right to your soul. I could spot those eyes from across a crowded room. I had no doubt which soldier was mine, even though they all resembled each other in their green uniforms.

The time seemed to drag on for me after his few day's home. I was lonely in that little apartment.

Struggling to have any energy, I slept most of the time and ate the rest. I was gaining a significant amount of weight with my pregnancy, and I was always sick. I was miserable, and not seeing Chance made it worse.

By the time Chance had completed all his training, I was about to give birth to our first child. I spent my entire pregnancy alone. Chance only got to experience about a month of my pregnancy, the last and worst month before I went into labor while he was home on leave. I endured twenty hours of labor before we welcomed our first child, a boy we named Adam.

My mother and the boys were in the waiting room when Chance announced the arrival of Adam. My mother and Chance hugged, and then Chance patted Matthew on the back and said,

"You are an uncle. Congratulations!" He walked back towards the maternity ward with an extra pep in his step. He was proud.

Chance was briefly home with Adam and me before the Marines assigned him to his permanent location in Jacksonville, North Carolina, Camp Lejeune. It was a new place for us both, but we were looking forward to the warm climate since we both grew up in Indiana, where the winters could be cold and grey. Neither of us ventured out of Indiana much. Traveling took money, and our families did not have money. It was an exciting new adventure for us, and we could not wait.

Chance's duffle bag was hanging from his shoulder with his tightly rolled shirts and pants inside, preparing to hop onto a Greyhound bus headed south.

"I will send for you and Adam once I can secure base housing." Chance says as he kissed us both on the forehead.

"Not much longer, sweetheart, and we will all be together." Chance turned to step onto the bus.

I spent the next few months tending to Adam, waiting for Chance to send for us, and although my mother frequently visited to help me with anything I might have needed, for me, it seemed like it was taking forever for Chance to call, requesting our arrival. What I did not know is that Chance was not working that hard to get us there. He was a young man, barely 19 years old, and he was having one hell of a good time, living in the barracks, eating at the mess hall, and spending his money how he wanted.

Although Chance was married with a child, he was having difficulty getting into base housing because he could not stay out of fights on and off base. He was a bit of a hell-raiser, even tattooing Hell Raiser on his forearm. He was spending his days of leave drinking with the single military men, chasing women, and stirring up trouble in the local town. He was making a name for himself and not a good one.

One afternoon his Commanding Officer summoned him into his office.

"Chance, I understand you are causing a bit of trouble. This trouble will stop now, or I will have no other choice but to send you to the brig. Do I make myself clear?" Chance's CO says as he stands up from his desk.

"Sir, yes, sir." Chance replied as he saluted his CO.

"Dismissed."

Fearing a stint in the brig, Chance decided he better clean up his act. He also promised that he was going to send for our son and me. He failed to do that with all the things he involved himself in. It was time to change, grow up, and start acting like a husband and a father.

Adam was eight months old before Chance secured base housing. Longer than he or I expected, but the day came when I arrived with the car loaded down with what little we owned. Selling our handed down furniture before leaving Indiana and only bringing clothes and the things I needed for Adam.

"Man, am I glad to see you." Chance said as he embraced me before carrying in all my luggage and Adam's toys.

"This place seems nice," I said as I put my suitcase down.

"It needs a women's touch, but I am sure you have that covered. It's so good to see you, Rach." Chance put his arms around me, kissing me softly on the cheek.

The houses on the base were perfect square-shaped houses strategically placed with small yards in-between. It was where we would make our home for as long as the military allowed.

Chance and I settled into a routine. Chance would leave every morning to do his duties while I stayed home with Adam. In the evenings, we would spend time together playing with Adam, taking walks around the base, and meeting up with friends that also had children.

I met several other wives of service members in our neighborhood, which helped with the lack of family support. It was hard for me to be away from my friends and family, but I made the best of it, and Adam kept me busy.

Chance's duties would sometimes require him to be gone for a month or two at a time, leaving me all alone. When Chance would return, he would spend countless hours off base drinking and chasing women with the friends he made in his unit.

Before too long, I found myself repeating the same pattern I watched my mother in for so many years, trying to get a drunk husband to bed or finding him passed out in the yard where his buddies left him the night before. Night after night, I would try to get Chance into bed. Enduring drunken insults as I tried to help him up on his feet.

"Bitch, leave me alone. You don't even know who I am." Chance slurred as he stumbled down the hall.

"Do you know how powerful I am? I can make shit happen around here." Chance continued as he bumped into the walls.

"I am sure you can," I responded sarcastically. "But for now, you are going to bed. Can you try to be quiet, so you don't' wake the baby?" I asked as I guided him down the hall.

Chance's drunken outbursts continued, and his constant brawls at the local bars did not let up either. I found myself mending wounds and black eyes that Chance brought home with him regularly. I did not know how to make him stop the drinking or the fighting. At this point, he was not hurting me. I only saw it as a nuisance to my daily life. He was still going to work and providing for us, so I dealt with it, just like my mother did.

Weeks turned into months, and I contemplated leaving Chance many times, but I too found myself with a child and no job to support us. I felt stuck. Watching my mother endure what she did from my father, I knew this was not how I wanted to live or how I wanted to raise my child. I was stronger than her, smarter than her, and I would be damned if I were going to live the life she lived with a drunken bastard.

Chance's insults turned into pushing and shoving and occasionally flicking me on the back of the head with his fingers as I passed by, a reminder of how my father did the same thing to me as a child. I was living in a home with a drunken man who would turn violent at any given moment. I felt the same feelings I felt as a child towards my father, feelings of hatred, resentment, and fear. I began to feel those same feelings towards Chance.

My life was not the life Chance promised me or that I dreamed about; it was similar to my childhood minus the sexual abuse. I wanted more.

Coming home after work, again, Chance was drunk and full of rage. The two of us began to argue back and forth about finances. Chance felt as if I was wasting his money, never having enough for the things he wanted to do.

"I don't know how you could spend so much damn money. All you do is sit on your fat ass all day doing nothing." Chance pointing and shouting at me as I sat on our black and white flower printed couch as he stumbled about, slurring his words.

"I don't just sit on my ass, Chance. I take care of this house and our son. It takes money to run a household." I responded, getting up from the couch.

"Do you think the laundry and cleaning take care of themselves? I do plenty and if you don't like how I do things, then do them your damn self." I pushed the basket of folded clothes onto the floor.

"What is that supposed to mean?" Chance followed me as I walked into the other room. I kept walking away, not responding. Chance grabbed me by the back of the head, pulling me towards him.

"I asked you a question. I expect an answer. What is that supposed to mean?"

"I am leaving you, Chance. I can't take this anymore." I sat down at the kitchen table sobbing. Chance kicked the leg of the chair I was sitting in, knocking me to the floor.

"You can't leave me. Where do you think you will go? Back to your daddy? Let him beat on you a little more?"

"I don't know where I will go. But someone will have me and do better by me than you."

"Then go, bitch. I don't need you, anyway." Chance said as he grabbed his jacket and headed out the door.

I picked myself up off the floor and began to pick up the folded clothes, refolding them as I put them in the basket. I didn't have a plan for leaving, but I thought I better make one. That was not how I wanted to live. I was unhappy, and I really didn't know if I loved Chance, but then again, I wasn't sure I even knew what love was. I should love him. I married him after all, but maybe marriage does not equal love and love doesn't equal marriage.

Things happened so fast between us. Before I knew it, we were married and having a child. We did not know each other.

53

We just both wanted to escape from our homes so bad that we latched onto each other and ran.

Chance went to his regular place off base and drank until he could barely stand up. The barkeep called him a cab, and when he arrived home, he stumbled into the house, yelling.

"Rachel, my love, where are you? Rachel, my love, where are you?" He repeated it several times.

Finally, I got up to find Chance sitting at the kitchen table with his 9mm in his hand, finger on the trigger.

"Oh my God, Chance. What are you doing? Put that thing away." I pleaded.

"No, come here, sweetheart, and sit down." Chance softly tapped the barrel on the table. I complied and sat down across the table from him.

"Chance seriously, put that away before someone gets hurt."

"I see it this way. You can't leave me, Rachel. No one is going to have you with a baby on your hip. You are overweight, and frankly, you aren't that fun." Chance babbled, moving his hands, and waving the gun as he talked.

"I am not sure if I even want to keep you. You don't even know if Adam is my son, do you? I have taken care of you both anyway, just like I promised. So, I think you should be begging me to keep you as my wife. You don't have it so bad, Rach."

Chance raised the gun and placed the barrel on my forehead.

"Get on your knees." Chance shoved the barrel harder, pressing it into my forehead.

"Get on your knees and beg me to keep you." Scared for my life, I began to cry as I slowly got on my knees in front of Chance.

"Please, Chance, Please, don't do this." I pleaded.

"Beg bitch, beg." Chance said, looking down at me.

My voice was cracking.

"Please keep me, Chance, please keep me." I was trembling with fear.

"Now, kiss my feet and tell me how much you love me." Chance gestured with the gun.

"I love you, Chance; I could never leave you." I complied and kissed his feet.

"Now get up and give me a kiss," Chance grabbed my arm, pulling me up from the floor. Crying uncontrollably, I leaned in to kiss him as he grabbed me and pulled me closer to him. Chance then forcefully pushed me away as he stood up and moved away from the table.

"You are pathetic." Chance turned, walking down the hallway towards the bedroom.

Once Chance fell asleep, I grabbed up baby Adam and headed a few houses over to a friend's house on base. I replayed the night's events to my friend as I sobbed.

"I don't know what to do. I don't know what to do; Chance could have killed me." I cried.

My friend suggested turning Chance into his CO. The military does not tolerate this kind of violence, even though they treat these cases the same as they do in civilian life. Chance would not have a record when he left the military if I reported him to his CO instead of the police.

It was late when I left my friend's home. I was worn out from the night's events and all the crying I had done. I needed to go to bed. As Chance got up for work the next day, he spoke nothing of the night before. He kissed me on the forehead and patted Adam on the head as he sat in his highchair. Chance headed out the door like he did every morning as if nothing happened. I realized Chance had no recollection of his actions, if he did, he was not saying. If he could not remember what happened then, that meant it was worse than I thought. I was in real danger. I knew alcohol could cause severe blackouts and memory loss. I watched it my entire childhood, and I knew exactly how dangerous it could be.

I made an appointment that same day to speak with Chance's CO. I explained the previous evening events in detail.

"I don't want to get Chance in trouble, sir, but I am scared that he doesn't remember what he does when he is drinking," I explained. "He may need some help." He listened to my concerns and assured me that he would take care of things. And he did. Chance's CO assigned him to ship duty for one month, that same afternoon.

Marines viewed this as punishment because they were not Navy men, and being on a ship with no women or alcohol was a punishment. Chance's CO hoped he would sober up and get a handle on things. It was not the first time his CO had a run-in with Chance, but he assured me it would be the last.

Having no contact with Adam and me for the entire month, only the other men on the ship could be just what he needed to get a handle on his life and his drinking.

Chance returned after his month of ship duty, sober with a clear mind. He was happy to see us, embracing us both as he walked in the door.

"Man, are you guys a sight for sore eyes. I have missed you both." Chance said as he hugged us tighter.

It appeared as if Chance was doing better. I could see the old Chance that I knew before the military. He was affectionate and kind, calling me sweetie and babe. Kissing me and holding my hand every opportunity he got. He even apologized to me for his actions before his absence.

"Sweetie, I am sorry. I wasn't myself, and that drinking makes me do some stupid stuff. Can you forgive me?" Chance grabbed my hand.

"I forgive you, but no more drinking," I replied.

"No more drinking." Chance agreed.

I gave Chance time to settle back in before I told him the news. While he was gone, I found out I was pregnant with our second child. I waited to see how he would act when he came home before I shared the news. I still was not sure if I was leaving him, so I did not want to tell him right away. Chance kept his promise not to drink. He was coming home each day after work, enjoying my company, and playing with little Adam.

It was a dream for me even though I still did not know if I was really in love with him. I certainly cared about Chance. He was the father of my children and the one person who took me away from my nightmare at home. I felt a bit of obligation to him because of those things, but I did not love him deep down.

  I told him about the baby anyway. He was the father, and as of right now, he was doing everything I wanted him to be doing as a husband and father.

  "Chance, I am pregnant again," I said abruptly as we ate breakfast.

  "That is wonderful, Rachel. Do you think we will have a girl?" Chance asked, looking up from his scrambled eggs.

  "I don't know, but I do feel different this time. So maybe it will be a girl."

  "That would be great, a boy and a girl. A perfect little family." Chance reached for my hand as he leaned in to kiss me.

  As the months passed, everything seemed great. We gradually started inviting friends over to our place to play cards and hang out. Little by little, Chance started drinking again. He would only have a couple of drinks before I would cut him off, reminding him of his promise to me. I did not want to see the Chance that I saw several months prior. I was trying to hold my family unit together, and I knew if he started drinking again, he would become unbearable, and I would leave this time. I forced thoughts out of my mind of that dreadful night when Chance put the gun to my forehead and made me beg. I was not going back to that life with him.

Even if it meant I would have to raise two children on my own, I had made up my mind. I would leave.

Chance was out on assignment when I went into labor with our second child. I took Adam over to a friend and drove myself to the hospital. The base hospital was only a couple of blocks away, so I figured I had time. I arrived at the hospital in plenty of time before the hard labor pains started. The nurse asked where my husband was and sent for him. I was not scared to give birth alone, but I sure did not want to. I just kept praying that Chance would make it before the baby came. I was scared. No matter how many children you have, the fear of birth never changes. I needed him. Chance arrived just in time. My ten-hour labor allowed only enough time for Chance to get a helicopter approved to fly him in. Chance ran into the delivery room, a few more pushes, and our baby girl arrived. We were delighted to have a girl to add to our family.

"I want to name her Angel. Daddy's Little Angel." Chance said with joy in his voice. I agreed.

Chance was so excited about having a little girl. In his mind, this was the perfect family he always dreamed of; he could not ask for more. Our life together was not idyllic, but we managed and tried to do right by Adam and Angel. We were becoming content with the life we had created for ourselves.

Chance found his path in the military, repairing heavy equipment. He enjoyed working with his hands, and he felt a sense of accomplishment, putting things back together.

I met several other military wives, whom I would meet up with several times a week at the park letting the children play while we visited.

All seemed to be going as planned, a perfect life until the day came. The day that Chance would have to decide if he was re-enlisting or getting out of the military.

Chance always thought the military was temporary. He never had plans to stay in for the long term. It was a way for him to get experience and provide for his family. A long-term enlistment never crossed his mind, and frankly, he forgot that his time was up.

"Rachel, we need to talk. Come sit down." Chance motioned to the kitchen chair.

"Is everything ok, Chance?"

"Well, we need to decide what we want to do. Do we stay, or do we go?"

"What do you mean?"

"My time is up here. I can re-enlist, or I can move on. I need to decide by Friday."

"By Friday! That's not much time to decide our future."

"I guess they figure we have had several years to think about that."

"I guess you are the one who has to decide what you want. I am not the one that the military will own. Ultimately, it is your decision."

"I am going to give it some thought. We will talk about it again tomorrow." Chance cupped my hand in his.

"Either way, it will all be ok."

Chapter 5
Home Sweet Home

The next day, Chance called his brother back home in Indiana to see what kind of work was available in that area. His brother assured him that there was plenty of work, and if all else failed, he could help him on his farm. Chance's brother even put him in contact with a friend who ran the County Highway Department. They had a couple of openings and were in desperate need of someone with mechanical skills. Chance fit the part so well that the guy hired him over the phone and told him he would put him to work as soon as he got back in town. Chance was happy to know he would have immediate employment.

When Chance got home, he told me the news.

"We are going home, sweetheart." Chance said as he put his coat on the hook.

"So, you have decided?"

Chance told me about the job opportunity at the County Highway Department. I did not say much. I was still trying to process how our lives were about to change. I was happy to go home and be around family, especially my brothers, but I would miss the other mothers I met on base. I was not sure if I would have the same support system there, none the less we were going home.

Once Chance put in for his discharge, it took about two months to get everything processed. In the meantime, I began packing and preparing for the move.

We had not secured a place to live in Indiana yet. I was unsure how much to keep or get rid of, even though we did not have a lot.

"Chance, we need to try to find a place to live right away. I do not want to live with my parents or your parents." I said as I wrapped glasses in the newspaper, placing them in a box.

"I know, sweetheart, I don't want to live with them either. Why don't you call your mother and see if she will send you a newspaper? Maybe that way we can have an idea of what is available for rent before we get there. We can even have appointments set up to see some places in the first few days." Chance continued as he sat down on the floor with me and started helping me wrap glasses.

"That sounds like a good idea. I will call her."

The next day I called my mother and asked her to send the Sunday paper. The Sunday paper always had more in it than the rest of the week, and most landlords waited to put ads in the Sunday paper because the ads were so expensive.

When we received the paper, Chance and I scoured the for-rent ads hoping to find the perfect place. A few phone calls later, we arranged several viewings for the first week when we arrived. I was relieved. I did not want to spend any more time around my father than I had to. I had a hatred for him that I had suppressed for many years, and the less time I was around him, the better off I was going to be. I also did not want my children to be around his drunken outbursts or fits of rage. We needed to find a place as soon as possible.

Before long, it was time to pack the U-Haul truck and head back to Indiana, where we both grew up. Chance drove the U-Haul, and I followed in our car we bought a few months earlier, a 1970 light blue Chevy Impala. It was a far cry from Chance's dream of having a sports car, but it was a practical family car.

The day and a half journey took a toll on everyone. We pulled over and slept when we could, trying to save money. The kids were hard to manage in a car ride that long. They were both getting fussy, and it was hard to keep them occupied. Chance and I made many stops on the way so everyone could get out and stretch and play for a little bit. We thought we could make the trip in a day, but the constant stopping took us much longer.

My mother anticipated our arrival, making up the spare room for us, and buying extra things at the grocery for the children. She was excited to see her grandchildren and me. My mother had only seen Angel one time prior when she and my father visited for a few days. She could not wait for us all to be home.

Chance and I pulled in the driveway a little before dinner on a Friday. Exhausted, we gathered up a bag with a few clothes and toiletry items so we could take a shower. My mother met us at the door and showed us where we could put our things.

I felt like a stranger in my parent's home. It was not such a bad thing, though, leaving those haunting memories behind. After leaving home, my mother and father bought a double-wide mobile home on a small piece of land closer to town. No matter where they lived, I could still feel that cold staleness that lingered around my father, and I did my best to suppress the hatred I carried for him.

Different house, but my father had that same spot he sat in at the kitchen table, drinking a beer and smoking a cigarette.

"Hi, Dad! We will not be here long. We are going to look at some places on Monday." I said as I put my hand on Adam's back, directing him down the hallway.

"Stay as long as you need. Sit down, Chance, and have a beer." My father motioned for Chance to sit down.

"Ok, just one. We need to get bathed and get the kids ready for bed. It's been a long trip." Chance pulled out a chair and sat down. I gave Chance a stern glance, making sure he didn't get too comfortable drinking with my father.

My father and Chance sat at the table, talking like old friends, while my mother and I got the children bathed and ready for bedtime. My father had a significant amount of respect for Chance after he joined the Marines. He saw it as a manly thing, and now they were on the same level.

"I have a roast on, and it is probably ready. Let's go eat, and then you can take a shower." My mother and I scooped the children up and went into the kitchen.

I remained quiet as we all sat down to eat. I was exhausted, but I was still unsure of my father, and I just wanted to stay out of his way while we were there.

It was clear he was drunk, just like he always was when I was growing up. Not much had changed. I shuttered at the sight of him, even though I was an adult and in control of our interaction. I still sometimes felt like that little girl who feared him. It was best I kept my distance.

64

The weekend came and went. Chance and I looked at several places and found a cute little house in town. It was affordable and just big enough for our small family. We took no time getting moved into it, even sleeping on the floor while moving our stuff in from the U-Haul. I figured we could manage. I would do my best to make it feel like home for us.

Chance started his job right away at the County Highway Department. He was their best mechanic and was fitting right into civilian life. It was as if he never left or lived the military life for a few years. It was not long, though, before he started stopping off at the local pub for a beer or two with the guys from work. Running into old friends who were still doing the same thing they were doing when Chance and I left our small town.

Within a couple of months of being home, I found myself trying to keep dinner warm for hours only to be disappointed when Chance would arrive too drunk to eat. He was passing out a couple of nights a week. Not from work exhaustion but his drinking.

Here I was again, repeating patterns. For some reason, I thought things would be different. Chance was out of the military and away from those friends, but nothing changed. He just found new friends who enjoyed doing what he wanted, drinking and fighting. I was home with the children all day, and when I did get to see my husband, he was too drunk to be of any use. I found myself helping him to bed or picking him up from the local bar when the barkeep refused to let him drive.

Local bartenders seemed to have our phone number on speed dial, calling in the middle of the night for me to pick Chance up because he was starting fights. Instead of having him arrested, they would call me. I would have to wake the children and put them in the car to pick up my drunk husband all hours of the night and early mornings.

His childish behavior infuriated me. After having two children, that wild side Chance had was not so attractive to me anymore. I wanted to settle down with our family, do family things.

I decided to get a job, and I secured an evening shift at the local state hospital. It was not a glamorous job, cleaning up vomit and feces, but it was a job, and I met people. It got me out of the house, and by the time I arrived home at night, Chance was already in bed passed out. Our interaction became limited.

Adam and Angel went to a babysitter while I worked, giving Chance all the time he wanted to stay in the bar. He spent much of his time there after work.

Chance and I rarely saw each other, and when we did, we were constantly bickering back and forth. Our marriage was falling apart. Any love between Chance and me had been lost. We both resented each other for various reasons. I resented Chance because he failed to keep his promises to me. Chance resented me because he felt he missed out on living it up during his young years, and deep down, he did not think Adam was his son, recalling the time frame in which I got pregnant and later gave birth. I never questioned it, but we were only together a few weeks before we married, so he doubted it and spoke of it many times. Our marriage was not what either of us imagined it would be.

Chance and I were not equipped to work through our problems, so we did our best to exist in the same home.

Chance let me handle all the finances, but I was terrible with money, so bills were going unpaid, which was unacceptable to Chance. He had always prided himself on having excellent credit, and he feared it was going to be ruined by my inexperience and carelessness with the bills.

"Why do we have a disconnect notice for the electric?" Chance, waving the bill in my face.

"I thought I paid that."

"You are the worst. It is not like we don't have the money, Rachel. You need to get this shit figured out. If I have to do everything, why do I need you?" Chance kept on.

"Do it your damn self. You don't do anything around here." I responded loudly.

"I work and pay the bills; I think that is plenty. You don't want for anything, Rachel. You have it made."

"I work too, plus I take care of the house, the kids and the bills. I do it all while you are busy drinking with your buddies. If anyone needs to get their shit together, it is you, Chance. I am so sick of this shit." I stormed off.

The fights continued as we went back and forth, blaming each other and pointing out each other's shortcomings. It was apparent our marriage was in trouble, but we continued to try and keep it together for the children. We were doing what we could and staying out of each other's way. Our marriage was a far cry from the fairy tale life that I had once dreamed of as a young woman. The life that Chance said he was going to give me.

I guess I did not know what to expect, but this was nothing like I imagined.

I started making friends and occasionally going out for a few drinks too. I figured if Chance could, why couldn't I? One evening I met some co-workers at a local bar. One of the maintenance guys' brothers played in the band, so we all thought we would support him. Chance hated live bands, so I knew there was no way of running into him. I needed a break just as much as he did, and the last thing I wanted was to see him out, starting a fight.

I had several drinks and danced like I was in High School. I was letting my hair down and having a great time. When the band took a break, my co-worker introduced everyone to Bryan, the guitar player. He was a few years younger than me, with blonde curly hair and blue eyes. He was an excellent musician, and I was impressed with his talent. He pulled up a chair next to me, and we began having a conversation about the music we both liked and whether he could play one of my favorite songs.

As the night went on, Bryan continued to sit next to me during his breaks. He bought me a few drinks, and we laughed and joked around the entire night. I had not had that much fun in a long time. I was so glad I went out and glad I met Bryan.

I did not want the night to end. Dreadfully I picked up the children and headed home. Of course, Chance was already in bed, having no knowledge of what time I came in. I tipped toed in the house and put the children to bed. Chance would be getting up in a few hours for work, so I laid on the couch instead of going to the bedroom, waking him.

I could not help myself from daydreaming the next day at work about the fun night and the nice guy I met. Chance made me feel as if I was fat and useless. Our marriage was falling apart, our sex life was non-existent, and I had low self-esteem. Chance reminded me continually of how much weight I gained having our children. Having someone talk nice to me was refreshing. I caught myself fantasizing about Bryan during the day. I imagined he would be all the things Chance was not.

I began joining my friends at whatever bar Bryan was playing at that night. My job required me to work on some Saturdays, so Chance was not aware that I was occasionally not at work but out enjoying Bryan's company.

Bryan became fond of me, too, joining me at the table during every break. Bryan knew I was married, so he did not make any advances. He was enjoying my company, and he enjoyed having someone to talk to during breaks from playing. I showed a lot of interest in his music, complimenting his talent and offering him a lot of attention. Bryan was doing the same with me. He was continually telling me how beautiful I was and how my husband did not know how lucky he was. We were having an affair, an emotional affair. I could not wait for each time I would get to see him again, almost forgetting that I was married with children. I was falling for Bryan, and I had not even kissed him.

Chapter 6
The Beginning to the End

Bryan and I continued our emotional affair for several months, not crossing the boundaries of physical contact. Our encounters at the local bars turned into phone calls during the day while Chance worked. We were talking about anything and everything hanging on each other's every word. It was so wonderful to feel like I had a connection with someone. It was nice to have someone to talk to since Chance and I barely spoke to one another.

I told Bryan about my marriage and how I never felt love for Chance like I thought I should. I told him about my children and how I felt blessed to have them, but I feared leaving Chance, afraid I would never find someone to want my two children and me. I was not sure how I would make it financially. I explained that my marriage was more about convenience than about love.

Bryan assured me that he would love my children like his own. He had nieces and nephews and loved being around kids. He poured on the charm, similar to the way Chance did when we first met. The only difference was Bryan could not express things the way Chance did. I was married, and we both were reminded of that daily when we had to quickly hang up the phone or cut a conversation short. We both wanted more, but Chance was in the way.

Chance soon found out about my evenings out. It was a small town, and people talk. As far as I was concerned, I had not done anything wrong. Nothing that Chance was not doing as well.

One night after I got off work, Chance met me at the door. I was shocked to see him awake. It had been months since he was awake when I arrived home.

"So, are you cheating on me?" Chance yelling at me as I took off my shoes.
"Chance, I need to put the kids to bed," I replied.
"Put them to bed, and then we are going to talk." Chance said firmly.

I dressed the children in their pajamas and put them to bed. As I strolled toward the living room, I took a couple of deep breaths preparing for the fight that was about to break out.

"Chance, I am not cheating on you. I am enjoying myself with some friends, the same as you do."
"Then why in the hell am I hearing about some guitar picker you have been cozying up to?"
"He is just a friend, Chance, nothing more. I work with his brother."
"Well, you are going to stop hanging out with your so-called friend right now." Chance demanded.
"You are not going to tell me who I can have as friends. I am a grown woman, and I can talk to whomever I want." I said as I began to walk away.
"Don't you walk away from me; we aren't finished." Chance grabbed my arm and pulled me back towards him.
"Let go of me," I said as I flung my arm out of Chance's grip, accidentally smacking him in the face. Chance backhanded me across the face reacting to what he thought was a direct hit from me.

I fell to the floor, face stinging. I began to sob.

"I am sorry. I did not mean to hit you. You hit me, and it was just a natural reaction." Chance said as he kneeled next to me, helping me up. "I am sorry."

"Chance, I want a divorce. I am not in love with you, and I don't know if I have ever been in love with you." I wiped the tears and pushed myself up off the floor.

"We can work this out. It is not that bad. We have just hit a rough patch." Chance said as he tried to console me.

"We can't fix this, Chance. It's over."

I went into the bedroom and cried as I laid down to sleep. It was over, and it had been for a long time. I was ready to end things with Chance, but I just was not sure how. Chance stayed in the kitchen, drinking a beer and trying to make sense of our failed marriage. He did not want to get a divorce. He truly loved me, but he was not sure how to show me. He did not know how to be a good husband. All he knew was to be a provider, and he was. In his mind, he was doing everything right by me, providing me with a home, a car, and the finer things. To him, that was a successful husband, so why was it falling apart? Why was his marriage failing? I needed more from him. I did not know what that was, but something was missing, something he could not give me. I yearned to be loved, loved like men love women in the movies.

The next morning when I awoke, I realized my eye was black and blue and swollen from the hit I took from Chance the night before. I was embarrassed, calling in sick to work. Later that day, I received flowers from Chance, apologizing for his actions.

He did not mean to hit me, and he felt terrible that it happened. The flowers were a nice gesture, but I was through with our marriage and probably had been for longer than I wanted to admit. I just needed to make the moves to leave.

I had my usual conversations with Bryan throughout the day. I told him about my black eye and how I asked Chance for a divorce. Bryan did not want to seem overzealous, so he stayed neutral when talking with me about the situation.

"You don't need this, Rachel. If I can help in any way, let me know." Bryan said before hanging up the phone.

Later that evening, Chance and I spent some time discussing our issues. Chance reluctantly agreed to a divorce. He was devastated, but he did not want me to feel stuck. If I did not want to be with him, he would not force me to stay.

Chance agreed to move out of our home. It was easier for him to leave than the children and me, so he promised to leave as soon as he found a place to live. He would not need much, just a place to sleep and shower.

A few weeks later, Chance moved in with another guy from work. It was the best scenario for him. The two could share the bills and ride to work together to save on gas. Chance was not going to have much money left over, supporting two households.

Chance agreed to pay the rent for the children and me, but I would have to pay the utilities. Our separation was temporary until we either reconciled or divorced. Chance believed our marriage could be salvaged.

Maybe a brief break would do us some good, and I would reconsider.

I did not reconsider. I had known for a while that I was not in love with Chance. It took me meeting someone else to help me realize that I was in a loveless marriage. I was not looking back. I filed for divorce.

Adam and Angel were still young. Adam 5 and Angel 3. Adam was in preschool and would-be starting Kindergarten in the spring. I found a reliable and cheap babysitter for Angel that was close to my work. Things seemed to be coming together.

While I focused on the divorce, I resisted spending time out. I did not want to risk Chance fighting me for custody of the children, so I laid low. Spending most of my time at home with the children, Bryan and I's friendship was mainly phone conversations.

Chance picked the children up on the weekends for a few hours, spending most of their time at his parent's home or the local park. His place was small and not a great layout for small children. Chance missed the children and me; he still wanted to be a family.

Dropping the children off at home, Chance asked me if we could talk. I sent the children to their room to play while the two of us sat down on that same flower printed couch we moved from North Carolina.

"Rachel, I miss you. I miss being with all of you. I need my family back. Please do not go through with the divorce. I can do better." Chance kept on as he reached out, touching my arm.

"Our marriage has run its course, Chance. Neither of us have been happy for a long time.

It is just best that we move on and try to make the best of it for the children." I replied, pulling away from him.

"If this is what you want, then I will agree, but I need you to know that I don't want it. I love you. I have always loved you. You and the kids are my whole world, and I am not the same without you." Chance began to tear up.

"I will get out of your way. If this is what you want."

Chance stood up and headed towards the bedroom where the children were playing. Trying to hold back tears, he reached down and picked Angel up. He squeezed her tightly, kissing her several times on the cheek.

"See you later, baby girl. Daddy loves you." He kneeled on the floor, sitting Angel back down, and reached over to Adam.

"See you next week, champ," Patting Adam on the head. "I love you guys."

Tears welled up in Chance's eyes as he walked down the hall towards the living room where I waited on the couch, giving him time to tell the children goodbye.

"I love you too, Rachel. A divorce will not change that. I will pick the kids up next weekend, same time."

Chance softly closed the door behind him. He sobbed that uncontrollable sob as he got into his car and drove off, hitting his fist against the steering wheel.

"FUCK!" Chance yelled.

The divorce did not take long to finalize since we agreed on most things. Chance was to pay child support and help with daycare, visiting with the children every other weekend and rotating holidays. It was over. Chance was devastated, and I was relieved. We went our separate ways, doing our best to be parents to Adam and Angel.

Chapter 7
New Beginnings

I started going out again to watch Bryan play music once my divorce was final. I even followed him to a couple of other towns where he played in their local bars. Chance kept the children for the weekend every other week, so I had more time to myself and more time to get to know Bryan.

After a few weeks of hanging out with Bryan, I invited him over one night after his set at Clancy's, the local tavern. I was nervous. I was with Chance for the past six years, and I did not date much in High School. It was new and exciting, but my insecurities made me question myself and my romance with Bryan. I made sure the house was spotless and everything was in its place. Bryan arrived just after 3 am.

We cuddled on the couch, the television on in the background, talking until the sun started peeking through the curtains. Bryan leaned in to kiss me, gently cupping my face in his hand. The kiss was passionate. I could not recall the last time someone kissed me that way. My body tingled all over every time he touched me. My hormones were running rampant, and a lump started to form in my throat. The passion was overwhelming. I never felt that kind of passion with Chance. This was a new experience for me. The kissing continued as we started caressing each other's bodies. Bryan ran his hands up my back unhooking my bra. I knew where this was all going, and so did Bryan. Several months of our emotional affair and built-up curiosity had us all over each other.

We moved from the couch to the kitchen, Bryan laying me gently onto the kitchen table as the kissing and touching continued. From the kitchen to the hallway, we made our way to the bedroom, stopping every few steps to steal another kiss. Bryan slowly started taking off my clothes as I struggled to remove his shirt. Giggling, he stopped and pulled it off himself, slinging it onto the floor. We said very few words to one another, only kissing each other passionately as Bryan pushed me onto the bed, straddling over me. We both had anticipated this moment for months, yet I was genuinely nervous. The sex was amazing. Bryan was a sensual lover, making sure he met all my needs. He was the best lover I had ever been with, even though there were few. I could not resist him. We laid in the bed, sweaty and exhausted. Bryan lit up a cigarette as he gazed into my eyes.

"I can't believe how well we fit together." Bryan softly brushed my hair from my face. "I have never felt this way about anyone before. I have waited my whole life for you." Bryan continued confessing his love to me, saying all the things he had been holding in for so long.

By this time, the sun was brightly shining and beaming through the gap in the drapes. It was almost 6 am. I got up and made us breakfast as we drank coffee and talked, touching, and kissing every chance we got. We were both overwhelmed with emotions. I do not know if love or infatuation was what we were both feeling, but we were feeling something, and it felt magical.

Bryan headed home, and I went to bed to rest for my night at work.

Neither of us could stop smiling. It was apparent
something had ignited in us both. Something neither of
us had ever felt. The passion, the laughing, and dancing
all seemed like a fairy tale romance to me. Could it be
real? Is this what love is? I had never felt this way.

No one ever saw me, saw me for who I was. My father
only saw me as his play toy, fulfilling his sexual desires or
his punching bag to take his anger out. Chance only saw
me as an escape and a person to play a role in his
fairytale. Bryan saw me for who I was. He saw Rachel,
and he made me feel important enough to be loved. I
never felt that way. I was overwhelmed with happiness.

Sex always felt disgusting to me. Because of the abuse
from my father, I only saw it as a duty. I did not realize
that I could enjoy it too until I met Bryan.

Slowly I was inviting Bryan over while the children
were home. Bryan took to the children immediately,
playing on the floor with them or taking them to the park
for the afternoon. He was right. He was good with my
children, and they liked him. I felt even more confident
about my relationship with Bryan seeing how good he
was with Adam and Angel. Could this be it, my shot at
happiness, love, and a normal family? Everything I had
always dreamed of, everything I had always wanted.

Chance, on the other hand, was not happy when he
found out that I had another man around his children,
but there was nothing he could do. Our marriage was
over, and I was moving on with my life.

My mother was not happy about it either. Bryan was
only 21, played music in bars for money, lived with his
alcoholic parents, had never been married, and did not
have any children of his own. What kind of life could he
possibly provide for the children and me?

My mother expressed her concerns to me, but I put up much resistance. I did not take any of my mother's advice; after all, my mother was still married to the man who molested and raped her daughter for several years.

"Rachel, what are you doing with him? He has nothing to offer you and the kids. You don't even know him. How are you going to let some strange man be around your kids?" My mother said firmly.

"First off, Mother, who I have around my kids, is none of your business. Secondly, you were never too concerned about who was around your kids." I shouted.

"Are we going back to that again? Rachel, you need to get over that."

"Get over it? Are you out of your mind? You don't just get over that, Mom. My father abused me for years, and you stayed with him. I will never get over it." I screamed, spit flying from my mouth as I cried an ugly, angry cry. "Get out of my house," I said, pointing at the door. "Get out!"

My mother and I fought many times about the abuse I suffered from my father and how she stayed and never confronted him. I felt betrayed. The one person who was supposed to protect me did not. My mother tried to protect me in other ways, making up for what she had done. If I got in a bind, my mother would bail me out. If I needed money, my mother found a way to give it to me. She enabled me to do whatever I wanted because she felt such guilt for what happened. She could not change it, she could not make it disappear, and she could not make me forget.

A few days would pass, and like always, my mother and I would start talking again. I was not giving up my lifeline, and my mother was not going to disown me. We were mother and daughter; as dysfunctional as our relationship was, we still stuck together.

My mother disagreed with my divorce from Chance. She felt we should have worked it out somehow. Chance was a hard worker and provider. He was a wonderful father and loved the children a great deal. My mother felt those things were all that mattered in a marriage. She was old school. She thought I needed to put my sexual desires or emotions aside for the sake of my children. Suck it up and do what was right for them and not myself. Become the sacrificial lamb for my family just like she did for hers. Maybe she was right, but I wanted more from a relationship, a marriage. I wanted to have a fulfilling relationship. I wanted to feel like I was someone's everything, cherishing our life together. I believed that I deserved to be happy and feel loved, and I thought I found it in Bryan.

Bryan was young and did not have much going on for himself. He was a talented musician, but it was not enough to pay the bills, and it was unlikely he would make it big playing in the small-town honky-tonks in rural Indiana. It seemed glamorous to me at the time, but his future was not very bright.

I was managing financially. I was able to pay the bills with my job, and Chance paid child support to help with the children. I was not too concerned about Bryan's financial situation. I was caught up in the moment, the excitement of being the musician's girlfriend that everyone knew in the local bars.

The romance and passion I had with Bryan kept me from seeing clearly. I was living in the now. My mother wanted me to see what a future would look like with Bryan, but I could not think that far ahead. The farthest I was looking was to the next time I would be with Bryan.

Bryan began spending more and more time at my house. Almost as if he lived there. It was rare that he went home. Bryan had moved in, unofficially. I did not mind. Seeing Bryan every day made me happy, so we shacked up, and I let him slide on paying any bills. We had not discussed him moving in, so for now, he was still a guest.

Bryan and I continued our romance despite everyone's disapproval. He helped me with the children in the evenings while I worked, staying with them after I tucked them into bed. I did not need a babysitter when Bryan was there, so he became a permanent fixture in our home.

No one liked the idea of me leaving the children with Bryan. My family and even Chance thought it was risky. He was a stranger, he was young, and he had no business being a babysitter. I ignored their constant complaints and continued to live as I pleased. I loved Bryan, and I knew how he was with my children and all his nieces and nephews. I did not see any reason why he was not capable of sitting with them at night. Especially since he was not paying any bills, it helped me out.

Several months had passed, and Bryan was still sleeping at my home and keeping an eye on the children. I knew it was time for us to take things further. I was not sure how Bryan felt about our relationship. He confessed his love to me but was he ready to move forward?

Our love affair looked like something you would see in the movies, just like I imagined. We would hold hands on the couch, gazing into each other's eyes for hours. Bryan would play his acoustic guitar for me, singing love songs, making love to me with his eyes as he belted out the words. I felt like the luckiest girl on the planet when I was alone with Bryan, but the reality was we had to have a conversation about our future. A conversation about where things were heading with us. Was this just a wild romance that would soon end? Was I just another girl Bryan had won over with his charm to have free room and board? All these things ran through my mind as I prepared to have the "conversation" with Bryan.

"Bryan, honey, let us talk for a minute. I love hearing you play your guitar, but while the kids are at Chance's, I thought we should talk." I placed my hand on the strings of Bryan's guitar to stop him from strumming.
"Okay, babe, what's up?" Bryan takes his guitar and leans it up against the wall where he always kept it. "Wait! If this is going to be deep, I need to smoke a joint." Bryan lights up a joint, closing his eyes as he blows out the smoke. "Here, take a hit. It will take the edge off." Bryan handed me the joint.
"I don't smoke pot, Bryan. You know that." I pushed Bryan's hand away.
"Maybe you should. Just try it." Again, Bryan handed me the joint.
"Just this once." I grabbed the joint from Bryan, trying not to burn my fingers.
"Just inhale and hold it for a second and then exhale." Bryan coached me along as I inhaled and then began coughing uncontrollably. The taste was awful.

"Let us get you something to drink. Next time just take a little hit. "Here, take a drink." Bryan handed me a coke to soothe the cough. "Try it again. Smaller inhale this time." I took a smaller hit, this time no coughing. "Now hold. Okay, blow it out. You just smoked your first joint."

"Wow, I am pretty relaxed." I leaned back, resting my head on the back of the couch. "So, this is why people smoke this stuff. I kind of get it." Gazing up at the ceiling, I felt a calm come over me. A peace that I had never felt before. It was like everything was right with the world at that moment.

"Yeah, I have been smoking for years. It helps me to be creative with my music. I don't get nervous on stage if I smoke before a performance. I don't need much, just a hit or two to calm my nerves." Bryan continued as he finished up the remainder of the joint. "We were supposed to talk, Rachel. You ready to talk now?" Bryan grabbed my hand, turned towards me as we both slumped into the couch in a relaxed state. Above us hung a tapestry with dogs playing poker. The decorations in my home were sparse. Everything I owned was mixed matched garage sale items I picked up from time to time. My decorating skills were lacking.

"I just want to know where we are going with this."

"Going with what?" Bryan asked.

"Our relationship. What are we doing? Are we a couple? What are we?" I kept on.

"I thought we were cool. I practically live here. What more do you want to know? Bryan responded, getting up to get a drink from the kitchen.

"I need to know if there is a future with us." Are you living here?" I asked.

"Do you want me to live here? Do you want a future together? Are you asking me because you aren't sure? Or are you asking me because you want to know how I feel?"

"I want to know how you feel about us."

"I have told you I love you. I love your kids too. Like they are my own. I am not seeing anyone else. Is that what you want to know? If we move forward, some things will have to change. But I like being with you."

"I want to move forward. What things have to change to do that?" I perked up, awaiting Bryan's answer.

"We can't live here anymore. Living in your and Chance's home doesn't seem right to me. Also, I think we should be married before we officially move in together. That only seems right, being you have children." Bryan continued as he watched my face with every remark he made.

"Married! Whoa, wait, I never said anything about marriage. Do you want to get married?" I perked up.

"Sure! Why not? You love me, don't you? I know I love you. We want to be together, so why not get married?" Bryan took a drink of coke like it was no big deal.

"I agree with you, Bryan, but you know I can't have any more kids. What if you want kids someday? I can't give them to you. You are young and having a wife and a family is a lot of responsibility. I am not saying you can't handle it. It's just a lot to think about."

"Look, Rachel, I love those kids of yours. I have all I could ever need right here. I will get a regular job and play music on the weekends. It's no big deal. In the meantime, we can start making plans to find another place to live.

85

We can tie the knot when we are ready. But for now, I want to kiss that beautiful face of yours and tell you how much I love you." Bryan grabbed me, pulling me close to him. He kissed me as if he were sealing the deal.

Chapter 8
Deja Vu

  It was late in the evening; the stars freckled the sky, and the moon illuminated the darkness. Outback of the local honky-tonk where Bryan was playing music that night stood Bryan, and I admiring the beauty above us as we shared a joint with a few other band members and their girlfriends. Smoke lingered in our huddle as we laughed and joked, making fun of the old ladies dancing and the local drunk falling. I always enjoyed myself when I was out watching Bryan play. Even though I would be overcome with jealousy when the groupies would dance in front of the stage, flaunting themselves at the band members, particularly Bryan. I knew I had to control myself. It was not the place, and I knew Bryan was going home with me. Those women were usually just regulars at the bar, hoping to hook up with one of the band members so they could say they were with the band. I knew Bryan had no interest in them, but it still bothered me.

  On the nights I could not join Bryan, I laid awake worrying about those other women, fearing that one of them would take my man. Stressing that he was spending his breaks enjoying the company of some other girl just like he did with me. I could not believe how jealous I was over Bryan. I never had that kind of jealousy over Chance. Did I ever love Chance this way? I did not think so. Maybe it was a way of knowing it was true love.

  I waited up for Bryan to come home. He still was not "officially" living in my house, but he was there every night.

I got up to greet him as he walked through the door. Every hair on my head was in place, and my makeup freshly done, awaiting his arrival.

"Hey, babe! How was it tonight? I got up from the couch and kissed Bryan.

"It was great. The crowd was big tonight. Johnny has us playing some new tunes that everyone was digging. I think it went well. They want us back in a couple of weeks." Bryan responded as he flopped down, putting his feet up on the coffee table. "I am beat, though."
I went into the kitchen to fetch an ashtray and a cold coke for Bryan.

"Hey, babe!" I yelled from the kitchen. "I think I am ready."

"Ok! Ready for what? Babe, the kids are here, and I am tired. Can we do this another night?" Bryan responded. I laughed as I came out of the kitchen with Bryan's coke.

"No silly, I am ready to get married."

"Far out! Let's do it. I don't think we can find anyone tonight to marry us but let's do it." We both laughed as we leaned in to kiss.

"The lease is up here, so I am going to start looking for a place. Maybe next month we will have a place that is ours, and then we can make it official. How does that sound?"

"Sounds like you have thought a lot about this. I trust you. You will find the right place. I can't wait." Bryan winked at me. I could tell Bryan was tired, and it was late, so we left the conversation at that.

After Chance and I divorced, I did not think I would ever get married again. I just knew it was going to be different with Bryan, though. We were great together. I was head over heels in love with him.

I did just what I said. I was on a mission to secure a place to live so we could get married and have our own home. This time I wanted to get married, not to escape anything, but to be with the man I loved for the rest of my life.

I found a small upstairs two-bedroom apartment not far from downtown. It wasn't far from work either, and I could easily afford it. Bryan and I still hadn't talked about what he was going to do for work; nonetheless, I pressed on with my plans.

A few weeks later, it was official. We were living together in a small apartment. Adam and Angel were almost six and four, so the two shared a room. It was cramped compared to the house we just moved out of. The one Chance and I found when we moved back home to Indiana. We agreed we would make do with the small space until Bryan could secure a full-time job. It was temporary.

My grandmother's hand-stitched quilt hung in the doorway, acting as a door for Bryan and I's bedroom. We could hear Adam and Angel laughing as they jumped on the bed behind the blanket. On the other side stood my mother, Matthew, Bryan, and I and a pastor from the church down the street. Bryan and I were tying the knot. Dressed in our everyday clothes, we kissed, and that was it. We were married.

My mother and Matthew both tried to talk me out of marrying Bryan. I would not listen, so they agreed to stand as witness to the marriage with much hesitancy. It was my life. They just hoped I was making the right decision.

Bryan had no job skills. He was still relatively young and had dropped out of High School, wanting to pursue his dream of playing music. He occasionally worked with his father repairing old coal furnaces, but the manual labor was just not for him. His hands covered in suet and ash took a toll on his ability to pick his guitar. Drying and cracking his fingertips. He was not going to take a chance on ruining his playing hands.

Bryan spent weeks searching for a job, but it was becoming a challenging task with no real skill. The food industry was not for him, and he needed to keep weekends open to continue playing music with his band. That was his dream, after all.

I was becoming frustrated with Bryan's inability to find employment. Bryan generally spent the little bit of money he made playing music on guitar strings and his smoking habits. He did not contribute to the household bills, putting all responsibility onto me, and I became stressed and overwhelmed.

"Bryan, you have to find work. I cannot keep paying all the bills. It's too much, and I am not making enough to pay for everything."

"I know, babe. I am trying. I am putting in job applications every day; I don't know what else to do other than enlist in the Army.

Didn't you say it worked out well for you and Chance when he joined the Marines? There is no war right now, and I could join for a few years to learn a trade. Plus, Elvis was in the Army." Bryan laughed as he inhaled a cigarette.

"Do you want to do that? We will have to move away from everyone. I am not sure how Chance would take it, me taking the kids away and all."

"I will go talk to the recruiter tomorrow. I guess we can decide after."

Bryan did not want to join the Army, but he was trying to be the man he promised me he would be. He needed some training, and the Army would take him without a diploma. They would teach him a skill or at least give him consistent employment. It seemed like the only thing to do at the time.

I did not mind the military life. I started getting used to it before Chance, and I decided to come home. I knew Chance would not be happy about it, though. I would take the kids away, and it could be far depending on where the military would station Bryan. I did not look forward to telling Chance.

Bryan took the tests for the Army. He scored low, so he was going in as infantry. Bryan was going to be a grunt until he could develop some skills. His basic training would take place down south, moving onto his specialized training and eventually finding out his permanent station. Again, I was home alone for weeks waiting to hear where we would soon be living.

The weeks went by quickly for me. Much quicker than they did when Chance was gone for basic training. I was working and taking care of the children, so the time seemed to fly.

Bryan and I would talk as often as we could. Bryan hated every minute of his training. It was the first time in his life he had structure. Bryan missed playing music, and of course, missed the children and me. He was counting down the days until he would be home with us.

"Hey babe, I got my orders today. We are going to Fort Riley, Kansas."

"Kansas! How far is Kansas from Indiana?"

"I think it is about 700 miles. My training will be over in a couple of weeks, and then I will be on leave for 30 days. Maybe we can drive over and see how far it is. I have to go, babe; my time is up. I will talk to you soon. Love you!"

After we hung up the phone, I started dinner for the children. I was unsure how to tell Chance that I would be moving the children 700 miles away from him. I paced around the kitchen, talking to myself as if I were talking to Chance, trying to figure out the best way to break the news to him.

A couple of days later, Chance arrived to pick up the children.

"Chance, we need to talk about something; it's important. Do you have time now, or do you want to wait until you drop them off on Sunday?"

"We can talk now." Chance took off his coat, and reluctantly sat down on the couch that used to be his. A look of disgust came over his face as he glanced over at Bryan's guitar. The children were outside playing when I broke the news to Chance about our move.

"We are going to be moving soon. Bryan has been in Army basic training the past month or so, and he just got his orders, Fort Riley Kansas."

"Kansas! Rachel, that is like 10 hours away from here. When will I see my kids?" Chance ran his fingers through his hair. He was heartbroken, knowing his children would be so far away. Adam and Angel meant everything to him.

"I know this is hard, but we will make it work. Maybe the children can come for the summers or breaks from school. We had to do something, Chance. There isn't much work around her."

"Rachel, there is work here. Just not for that guitar picking loser you married. Now I am paying for your choice to marry that bum."

"That's not fair, Chance. Bryan is a good guy, and he cares about the kids and me. Give him a chance. He is trying."

"I cared about you and the kids too, Rachel. I also provided for you. What is he going to be able to do on an E1 salary? He could have made that kind of money working in a restaurant. I cannot believe you are doing this to me. Don't you think you have broken my heart enough? Now this, now you are taking my kids away from me. You give your whole life to someone, for what? For them to take everything important from you. I cannot believe how fucking selfish you are. Where are the kid's things? I think this conversation is over."

"Chance, we will need to talk more about this. We only have a month." I grabbed the bag and handed it to Chance, kissed the children as they skipped out the door.

"Oh, we will be talking more about this, alright, but you will be talking to my attorney next time." Chance grabbed the doorknob to close the door. I grabbed the door, pulling it back open.

"Chance, don't do this."

"Bye, Rachel. I will have them back Sunday." Chance looked back at me and then slammed the door shut.

I wanted to make it work. I was not trying to take the children from their father, but I was trying to start a new life.

Chance consulted with an attorney; only there was nothing he could do unless he could prove I was unfit. He had to let us go. He could take me back to court to modify the visitations, but other than that, he had no choice. Chance was devastated and pissed.

I allowed Chance to see the children as much as he could for the next month. He would pick them up almost every night for a couple of hours. Chance knew it would be a while before he would get to see them again, and he wanted to make sure he spent as much time with them that he could.

The move was beyond Chance's control, and he was not dealing with it very well. All he wanted was to make sure his children did not forget him and that they knew how much he loved them. I understood. I was trying to do whatever I could to soften the blow of us leaving, but I knew it was breaking his heart. I felt terrible about it and bad for him.

On the last day Chance had with the children, he took them to the park and then to the Dairy Queen for an ice cream cone.

The children were too young to understand what was going on, so he resisted saying anything to them about the situation or letting them see how hurt he was. He wanted it to be the best day, so they would always remember it. He was not about to cry in front of them. That was not what he wanted them to remember.

As he approached our house, he could feel a lump form in his throat. He had to control his emotions for their sake, but his heart was breaking. He picked each of them up individually and gave them the longest hug he could.

"Daddy loves you, champ. Don't you ever forget it." Chance said to Adam as he hugged him and then put him down on the sidewalk. "Come here, baby girl." Chance picked Angel up and squeezed her tight.
"I love you, my little angel. I am going to miss you both very much." Chance choked back tears as he turned to head towards his car.

"Chance, I will call you when we get to Kansas," I said as he walked away. Chance threw up his hand as confirmation he heard me.

Chance drove off, but he did not get far. He pulled into the post office down the street, put his car in park, and began sobbing. His whole life was standing on that sidewalk, and there was nothing he could do but drive away. Deep down, he knew it could be a long time before he would see his children again. He held his hand over his heart and rested his head on the steering wheel. The pain was so intense that he felt like his heart literally broke in two.

Chapter 9
A Tragedy

We ventured to Fort Riley Kansas. It would be quite the adjustment, but the children were young, so they had not settled into a regular school system yet. They could easily adjust.

We rented a two-bedroom trailer in a small trailer park a few miles from Fort Riley army base. It would do for now, and I would make it home with what little we had.

Bryan made some friends while in basic training and one of those friends, Hank, rented a place two trailers down. Both of them were pleased when they got word that they would be working on the same base. At least they would know someone once we all arrived.

Hank and his wife were close to the same age as Bryan and me. They had a young boy who survived the death of his twin during birth. They were also newly married when Hank signed up for the Army. The four of us became quick friends, and we were spending many nights together. Hank was a large man, standing 6'5 and as solid as they come. Hence his nickname Tank. He towered over Bryan and often teased him about his small stature. Bryan was maybe 5'10 and only weighed about 160 lbs.

After a few drinks, the two would laugh and joke while Tank wrapped his massive arm around Bryan, putting him in a chokehold and then rubbing his head with his knuckles like brothers do to each other. Bryan did not mind the teasing; he had older brothers and was used to it. He looked up to Tank and was happy to have a close friend so far from home.

The guys spent every day together, working in the same unit. Us girls would hang out during the day watching soap opera TV or lying in the sun while the children were at school. We all became very close. We also began experimenting with different drugs while partying on the weekends. Bryan and I were already smoking marijuana regularly, but Tank and his wife started introducing us to pills, cocaine, and acid. Every weekend we were partying at one or the other's trailer. Playing cards and listening to Bryan play his guitar. Everyone singing along as if we were in a band. It was 1970's karaoke. We were young, and we were having a fun time together.

Financially Bryan and I were struggling. Chance was right. The E1 salary Bryan was making was not enough to take care of a family. We were barely getting by, and it began to put a lot of stress on our marriage. Our once wild romance began to crumble as we continually fought about finances.

Fighting almost every day caused a tremendous amount of tension in our home. The extra cost for our marijuana and occasional cocaine use did not help either.

"Brian, the electricity is going to get cut off if we don't pay at least half the bill this month. We only have $24 to our name until next month's paycheck. What are we going to do?" I explained as I handed the bill to Bryan.

"I don't fucking know Rachel. Maybe you should get a job and stop laying around smoking pot all day, doing nothing." Brian said, kneeling by the couch, reaching for the tray we stashed underneath where we hid our supply. "Where are the fucking joints I rolled last night?"

"What do you mean laying around all day? Oh, here we go. I support your lazy ass for the last year, and now suddenly, you are a saint because you have income coming in."

"Where are the fucking joints, Rachel?" Bryan yelled.

"I smoked them. There is a roach in the ashtray. Smoke it!"

"You fucking Bitch!" Bryan picked up the ashtray and threw it at me, barely missing my head. "You know I can't smoke all day. You couldn't save me a joint for when I get home? You fucking fat ass bitch."

"Brian, you almost hit me."

"Well, I guess I need to practice my aim. I am going to Tanks." Bryan walked out, slamming the rickety trailer door behind him.

I cried as I picked up the cigarette butts and swept up the ashes from the floor. The children arrived home from school just as I finished cleaning up the mess. The school bus was packed with military kids, and it usually took about an hour for the children to arrive home.

"Hey, kiddos. How was school today?"

"Good!" They both answered.

Adam and Angel put their bags down and headed outside to play. Our neighborhood was full of other children, so they would go out to play every day after school until it was time to come in for dinner. I was so glad they were adjusting well.

I looked out the window to check on the children when I saw Bryan walking back over from Tanks.

I braced myself for another blowup. Standing in the kitchen preparing dinner as if nothing happened, I looked over at Bryan as he walked through the door.

"Hey!" I said, looking up from the sink.
Bryan walked over and put his arms around me, softly kissing me on the back of my neck as I faced the window.
"Babe, I am sorry. I am glad the ashtray didn't hit you. I had a rough day. Can you forgive me?"
I turned around and kissed Bryan back.
"I forgive you. You are right; I need to get a job. I need to work, not just for the money, but I don't like being home, I get bored watching TV all day. And don't get me wrong, I like Char (short for Charlotte), but we do not have much in common other than you guys. So, I will start looking next week. We need to get another vehicle, though. That piece of shit out there is not going to get me far. I am sorry too."
"I know, Babe. I know you aren't lazy. I will talk to Tank about their other car. He was talking last week about selling it. Maybe he will let us make payments on it until we get the money. We will figure it out. I don't want to fight with you. Okay?" Bryan smacked me on the butt on his way to the living room.

Bryan talked to Tank about buying their second car. Char did not work, so they only needed one vehicle, and they needed the money too. The two agreed that we would pay $30 a week, paying it off once we got our tax return in a few months. In total, Bryan and I would pay $700 for the car. More than the car was worth, but Tank was willing to work with us, and we needed something right away.

I secured a job at a local nursing home a week later. It was not exactly what I wanted to do, but it would help pay the bills. I was able to work the morning shift, allowing me to get the kids off to school and be home before they got off the bus. Things were looking up.

The holidays were approaching fast, and we wanted to make sure the children had a few things under the tree. Being away from family made it hard around the holidays. It would be quiet for us because traveling home was not an option with little money and two vehicles that weren't in the best condition.

I made the best of it, cooking some traditional recipes my mother gave me before leaving home. Discovering I was a good pie maker, we had several for dessert.

Bryan and I managed to put a few presents under the tree. The children seemed happy with what they got from Santa, and Bryan was thrilled when he opened his gift from me, a 12-gauge shotgun I found at a local pawn shop. Bryan was excited and could not wait to try it out. Several of his buddies talked about Pheasant hunting, and now Bryan would be equipped to go. Bryan tried to plan a hunting trip with Tank, but Tank seemed distant since we bought his vehicle on payments. Their conversations were short, and they were spending less time hanging out together on the weekends. Bryan feared something was going on with Tank that he was not sharing.

Sitting at the kitchen table, cleaning his newly acquired gun, Bryan expressed his concern for Tank to me.

"Have you noticed Tank and Char acting strangely these days? Something is going on with him".

100

His work performance is down, and we haven't been hanging out like we use to."

"I noticed you guys hadn't been hanging out, but Char and I don't talk much now that I am working full time. I have noticed the distance ever since they got back from their trip back home to Ohio. Do you think something happened?"

"Rachel, I think he is on something. Something heavy."

"I hope not. Can you go talk to your CO and see if they might be able to help him?"

"I can't do that, Rachel. Are you crazy? I can't rat him out. What if it's nothing?"

"Maybe you need to sit him down and talk to him. We have to help him if he has gotten himself into something big time."

"I will try to talk to him this weekend. Let's invite them over for dinner or something." Bryan said as he continued cleaning his gun.

"I will call Char and make plans, but for now, you need to move your shotgun; it's time to eat."

I did not know that Bryan and Tank agreed to purchase some drugs to sell and split the profits. Tank put the money out for the drugs, but neither of them sold their share. Tank was out a lot of money; they both were using instead of selling their portion, and Tank was not happy about it.

One early morning in January 1979, Bryan and I woke up to banging on the trailer door.

"What the hell is that?" Bryan looked over at me.
"What time is it?" I asked.

"It's 2:30 in the morning." Bryan put his glasses on to see the alarm clock across the room.

"What the hell is going on?" Bryan pulled the curtain back, looking out the bedroom window but did not see anything. The banging continued down the trailer to the front door. Then we heard Tank outside yelling.

"Bryan, get your fucking ass up. We need to talk. I need my money." Tank continued yelling for Bryan. Bryan finally got a glimpse of Tank from the window and saw that he was clearly high on something.

"What the hell, Tank go home, it's 2:30 in the morning, and we can talk tomorrow."

"He is wacked out, Rachel. What do we do?" Bryan looked back at me from the window. Fear on his face.

"Don't open the door Bryan, he could hurt us."

"Open the door, you son of a bitch. I want my money." Tank continued to bang his fist against the trailer.

"Go home, Tank. You are scaring Rachel, and you are going to wake the kids. I am going to call the police if you don't leave." Tank stumbled away, mumbling obscenities.

Fearing Tank would return, I ran to a neighbor and called the police to report the disturbance. It was clear that he was on drugs. Stronger than the ones we partied with on the weekends.

"911, what's your emergency?"

"Hello! my friend was just here banging on our trailer. I think he is on drugs or something. He isn't acting right."

"Ma'am, do you want me to send out a unit?"

"No, I just wanted to call and report it in case he comes back," I explained.

"Do you think he will come back tonight?" Dispatch asked.

"I don't know, but he is angry, and he is a big man. We are scared. Our kids are in the house too."

"Ma'am, do you have any kind of weapons in the home? Any guns or knives you could use to protect yourself if he does come back?"

"I just bought my husband a gun for Christmas, but I hope it doesn't come to that. He is our friend."

"I understand, but keep your gun close. If your friend is on drugs, that may be the only way to stop him from hurting you and your family. Crack cocaine makes super humans out of people. If that is what he is on. Call back if you need us to send a unit out."

I hung up the phone and ran home where Bryan was on the couch, holding his 12-gauge shotgun. We were both in disbelief. Angel emerges from the bedroom, wiping the sleep from her eyes.

"Mommy, what is wrong?"

"Nothing, sissy, go back to bed. Everything is okay." As I guided Angel back down the hall, I heard a loud noise.

BOOM! BANG! BANG!

The front door flew open, the trim splitting from the frame.

"Where is my fucking money, Bryan?" Tank screaming as he walked over the busted door, heading towards Bryan. Bryan jumped up and began walking back towards the hallway.

"Tank, you are messed up, man. Go home. We will talk when you are straight." Bryan pleaded.

Tank continued towards Bryan, backing him up against the stove inserted into the wall. "Tank, I don't want to shoot you. Go home, man, just go home." Bryan's voice was trembling.

Tank laughed an eerie laugh, almost as if he were possessed.

"Shoot me, you pussy, shoot me." Tank continued his creepy laugh. "You won't shoot me." Tank inched closer to Bryan. Bryan held the gun up to Tank's chest, inches away from touching him.

"Tank, please go home. I don't want to shoot you." Tank moved closer.

BOOM! Tank dropped to the floor. Bryan laid the gun down on the table and fell to his knees.

"NO! I didn't want to fucking shoot you." Bryan yelled, cupping his face in his hands.

Tanks wife heard the shot and knew what just happened. Charlotte's scream was so loud we could hear it from inside. Her earlier attempts to stop Tank from coming over to our place did not work. She rushed through the door.

"No. Oh my God, Hank."

Char and I kneeled by Tank lying in front of the kitchen sink on a multi-color rug; we grabbed hand towels and began putting pressure on the wound. I grabbed a tablespoon and put it in Tanks mouth, trying to hold down his tongue as it rolled back into his throat. Tank was suffocating. The shot was close and must have punctured his lungs. The children stood in the hallway watching the chaos; shock on their sleepy-eyed faces, they stayed out of the way.

They just witnessed a horrific incident that their little minds were trying to process.

The police arrived, and soon after, the paramedics. As the EMT's worked on Tank, the police began taking pictures and writing their report. Bryan's face was emotionless as they carried Tank out on a stretcher. He was in shock. Char followed closely behind, jumping into the ambulance. It would be the last time we would lay eyes on each other. Hank (Tank) passed away before arriving at the hospital. He was only 20 years old.

As the police were asking us questions, Bryan's CO arrived with a van and several MP's. Bryan thought he was going to jail. Fortunately, my earlier phone call proved he was protecting his family. It was self-defense.

Bryan's CO and the MP's were there for our protection. Bryan and Tank were government-owned. They were military men, and it was their job to protect their property. Since Tank was in the same unit as Bryan, the military feared retaliation. They both had friends in that unit, possibly putting us in danger. Once Tank's family got word of the shooting, they could be out for revenge. The military wanted to try to prevent that.

"Are you taking me to jail?" Bryan asked his CO with tears in his eyes.

"No, you are not going to jail, but you are leaving. You and your wife need to gather up some things. Enough for a few days. Is there anywhere you can go until we can get you transferred?"

"Transferred!" I quickly turned to look at the CO.

"Ma'am, you have to leave. It is not safe here for you and your family. We have already started the transfer paperwork. We will know in a couple of days where you will be going. Pack some things for now, and we will send movers over to pack the rest."

Bryan and I looked at each other with fear, shock, and uncertainty. We had no idea where we were going or when we would be going. All we knew was we were going to disappear, never to return to Kansas again. A horrible tragedy just turned our world upside down.

Bryan and I both had several interviews with detectives. Our transfer would not take place until they arrested Bryan or cleared him. I do not know what made me make that call that night, but the local authorities cleared Bryan from any charges because I did. They determined it to be a justifiable homicide.
The case was closed.

Chapter 10
Fort Carson

The rolling hills and beautiful sunsets laid the backdrop for the base in Fort Carson, Colorado. Although it was still winter when we arrived at our new home, it was a beautiful sight. Everywhere we looked, we could see mountains topped with glimmering snow caps. The views were so different than the flat plains of Kansas we just left. It was breathtaking.

None of us spoke a word about the events that led up to our new transfer to Colorado. It was the military life, and we had to treat it as such. Like a war that had ended, you moved on, you did your best to put it behind you, and most importantly, you tried to forget.

The military secured an apartment for us off base. Our things were stacked in boxes when we arrived. As the four of us walked through the door to our new life, our faces were expressionless. We were there for only one reason. A tragedy we left behind.

I began going through our things, trying to find linens and toiletry items. We all needed a bath and sleep. The last few weeks of the unknown had taken its toll on all of us, but it was time to start over and make the best of it.

Bryan barely slept, waking up in a cold sweat every night from the nightmares. He killed his best friend, and the event repeatedly played in his mind. A song, a smell, or a sound triggered his emotions. He was crumbling.

He was sobbing throughout the day, struggling to look at himself in his uniform. A reminder of his friend that he worked beside in that same uniform.

He was trying to snap out of it, but he could not. Like a soldier coming home from war, flashbacks consumed his thoughts and his dreams. Bryan sank into a deep depression, overcome with a great deal of grief. He tried to figure out where he fit into society after such a horrible thing happened. The military offered no solutions and did not care about his struggle. They wanted him to fulfill his duty to the United States Army and forget about what happened. Move on with life.

Bryan decided to get out of the Army as soon as his time was up. He never spoke about the incident or Tank. Life continued, but Bryan was never the same. He had continuous nightmares and outbursts of anger, mostly towards me.

Fighting became normal for us. Bryan clammed up, and I was trying to find a way to help him cope, but we were drifting apart. I wanted to fix it, but I couldn't. Tank's tragic death happened, and it changed our lives forever.

"Bryan, I need you to talk to me. It's been months now, and you haven't even touched me."

"What do you want me to talk about, Rachel? I don't have anything to say."

"You need to talk to someone, if not me, someone." I reached out to Bryan as he quickly pulled away.

"I don't want to talk to you or anyone. Just leave me the fuck alone, Rachel. Can you do that?"

"Fine, I am taking the kids to the park. You can sit here and wallow in self-pity for the rest of your life, but we still have to live." I helped the kids with their jackets, and we headed out the door.

"Go fuck yourself, Rachel." Bryan flipped me off.

I returned with the children from the park and a stop at the local ice cream shop a few hours later. The children were tired and happy. Laughing as we walked through the door, our laughing quickly stopped when we saw Bryan sitting on the living room floor with a bottle of Bacardi Rum in his hand. His guitar shattered in pieces and a hole in the wall where he had thrown it. His eyes were red and swollen from crying; he was broken.

"Adam, take your sister into the bedroom to play. I will call you when it's time for dinner." I softly pushed the children towards the bedroom as they stepped over broken guitar pieces.

"Bryan, what happened?" I asked as I sat down beside him on the floor.

"I tried to play my guitar to take my mind off things." Bryan began to sob. "The only song I could play was Tank's favorite song. Remember how he used to sing so loud and off-key?" Bryan smiled and then cried some more. I began to cry and laugh with Bryan as we talked about how obnoxious Tank was.

"He couldn't sing a lick, but when I played that song, he thought he was the lead singer of the band." Bryan wiped his tears as I put my arms around him.

"I know he was your friend, our friend, but you didn't have a choice. Bryan, you were protecting your family. Tank was not in his right mind. You have to remember that."

"Rachel, don't you think I know that? Don't you think I have told myself that a million times? It does not help the fact that I killed my best friend. I slept beside him in the barracks.

109

We have shared meals. Hell, one time, we shared a toothbrush. When I didn't think I could make it on a run, who do you think pushed me? Tank. He would have picked me up and carried me if he felt he had to. He wasn't just my friend; he was my brother."

I embraced Bryan as we both cried. Bryan wiped his face and then jumped to his feet.

"I need to get this picked up before the kids get home."

I made a strange face at Bryan.

"Bryan, the kids are in the bedroom playing."

"Well, I don't want them to see what I did."

"Bryan, they already saw it."

I crawled around, picking up broken wooden pieces of Bryan's guitar. Bryan began mumbling. I grabbed his arm.

"BRYAN! STOP! The kids already saw this." I shouted at Bryan as if to snap him out of whatever delusion he was in. Bryan turned around, grabbed me by both arms, and slammed me into the wall. I covered my head as a shelf fell on top of me.

"Get out of my fucking face bitch. Can't you see I am trying to do something?"

I took a moment to catch my breath. Then I grabbed Bryan from behind.

"You don't ever fucking lay your hands on me, you son of a bitch."

Bryan broke away from me and turned around swinging, hitting me twice in the face and once in the chest. I fell to the floor, bleeding from my nose and lip. I grabbed my nose; blood flowed through my fingers.

"You bastard!" I yelled as I pushed myself up with one hand. I lunged toward Bryan. He pushed me back on the floor.

Adam and Angel came out of their room, screaming,
  "Mommy, Mommy! Daddy, stop!"
  "Go back to your room," I yelled.
I reached for the door handle to call for help. By this time,
neighbors were standing in the hallway and doorways,
already aware of the disturbance. Bryan grabbed me to
pull me back into the apartment when a man from down
the hall began running towards Bryan.
  "Get your hands off her, you piece of shit." Bryan bolted
down the hallway with the neighbor chasing him out the
main door and down the street.

  A neighbor woman from across the hall came over and
helped me clean up my battered face and blood-stained
floor. Shortly after that, the man from down the hall
returned. He had chased Bryan as far as he could with no
shoes and no shirt.

  "Ma'am, are you okay? I couldn't catch him, but we can
call the police, and I am sure they will find him."
  "No, no," I responded. "He is going through some stuff. I
do not want him arrested. He didn't mean to hurt me."
  I did not want Bryan arrested. I was hurt, but I knew he
was going through a horrible thing, and the last thing he
needed was to go to jail.
  "Ma'am, it's none of my business, but he will keep
hitting you. Do you have someplace you can go to?" The
neighbors kept on trying to convince me to call the
police.
  "I will be fine," I assured them.
  "I am in 116B if you need anything. 116B." The man
repeats.

The neighbor woman got Adam and Angel a bowl of cereal and sat them at the table as the other neighbors tried to help clean up the mess and tend to me.

"We don't have anywhere to go. We just got transferred here a few months ago. We were in Kansas before here. We are originally from Indiana." I explained to the neighbors.

"Ma'am, you can report him to the Army. They will take care of it." One of the neighbors said.

"I know. My ex-husband was a Marine. I reported him once. I do not want to do that, though. He is a good person. He is just going through a tough time. I am sure he feels terrible about what happened. I probably should have just given him his space. I know he did not mean to hurt me. This never happens." I responded, holding ice to my eye.

Realizing they could not help any more than they already had, the neighbors began going home.

"Thank you so much," I said as I hugged each of them as they left.

Hours passed, but there was no sign of Bryan. I was worried about where he might be since we did not know anyone in Colorado. I hoped that maybe he knew someone from work and was able to stay there for the night. I put the children to bed and prepared some ice for my black eye.

"Mommy, why did Daddy do that to you?" Angel said as I tucked her into bed.

"He was just upset. He did not mean to hurt Mommy. Don't you worry, Mommy is okay. Sweet dreams, sissy, I love you." I kissed Angel on the forehead and then tucked her tightly with the blanket.

I laid on the couch to rest. I could not sleep, replaying the night's events. Shortly after 1 am, the door opened. It was Bryan, sober, tired, and hungry.
I raised my sore body from the couch, not sure of what would happen. I wanted to be alert.

"Oh my God, Rachel. I did that to you? I am so sorry, baby." Bryan slowly walked over, reaching out to me, gently sitting down beside me. He began to cry.
"Baby, I am so, so sorry. I do not know what happened. One minute we were talking, and the next minute I am running down the street. I blacked out. I am not a monster, Rachel. Please forgive me." I quietly listened to Bryan explain himself.
"I know you are not a monster, Bryan. I cannot and will not live like this; you need to get help. I am sure in the hell not putting the kids through this. I know you are going through stuff, but if you don't talk to someone, it's going to ruin you, ruin us." I grabbed Bryan's hand and squeezed it. Shortly after that, we went to bed.
Bryan laid there holding me all night in a tight hold. He seemed so remorseful for his actions and for hurting me. I could not be mad at him. I should have just let him be, and maybe it would not have happened. I felt somewhat to blame.
Bryan laid low for a couple of months, trying to avoid the neighbors. He could not face them, knowing that they knew what he had done to me.

113

He never sought the help he needed to work through the tragic death of Tank. He figured in time, he would slowly forget and be able to move on. Bryan was afraid to reach out to anyone on base, unsure of what that would do to his position. He kept it to himself in the pit of his stomach and the back of his mind. On the one hand, forgetting made him feel like he forgot his friend but ignoring it drove him crazy.

I was right. Not getting help was ruining the person I fell in love with, and it was ruining our marriage. He was never the same person again. Not the same person I once knew. Every fight from that moment on involved pushing, shoving, name-calling, and throwing things across the room at each other. Every argument we had was heated, and no one could get Bryan's blood boiling more than I could. We were both numbing the pain with alcohol and drugs. I was trying to forget my childhood, failed marriage to Chance, and now dealing with Bryan's issues. Bryan was trying to forget he killed his best friend. Our once explosive love affair was turning into just explosive.

Bryan only had a few months left of his enlistment into the Army. He already knew he was getting out and was counting the days. Bryan had no plans for the future and did not know what he would do for work as a civilian. All Bryan knew was he was out, never seeing himself in that uniform again.

One night I drew myself a bath to soak in while Bryan shaved. I was trying to catch a few moments alone without the children.

"Bryan, you need to think about what we are going to do in a couple of months. Are we staying here, or are we going back to Indiana? What are you going to do for work?" I kept on as I washed with the bubbles from my bath.

"I don't know yet, Rachel. I am sure I can go back to playing music if we go back to Indiana."

"You can't play music for a living. It doesn't pay the bills. You need to have a stable job. Where will we live?"

"Stop fucking badgering me. I don't know." Bryan stopped shaving and pointed his razor at me. "You seem to have all the answers; you figure it out."

"No, that is your problem. You want everyone else to figure out your life. You need to step up and be a man. Quit waiting on everyone else."

Bryan snapped.

Bryan came over to the bathtub and put both hands on top of my head, pushing me down into the water. Holding my head under the water as I struggled. I flung my arms, trying to grab something to pull myself out. Bryan let up. I came up gasping for air.

"You son of a bitch. What is wrong with you?" I said out of breath. Bryan pointed the razor at me again.

"Don't you ever fucking tell me how to be a man. I will slit your fucking throat. I killed a man to protect you and your fucking kids. Don't you think that is man enough?"

"My fucking kids? I thought you wanted to raise the kids as ours? Or is that just what you say to make people think you are some kind of fucking hero?"

Bryan rears back his hand as if to strike me as I stood naked in a tub full of bathwater.

"Hit me, go ahead, hit me. I guess that makes you a real fucking man because you can beat on a woman?" Bryan backhands me; I go back against the wall, trying not to fall.

"See what you made me do? You just can't keep your fucking mouth shut." Bryan walked out of the bathroom and shut the door.

I steadied myself and got out of the bathtub. Trying to control my anger as I dried off. I have had enough, I said to myself. That bastard tried to kill me, which will never happen again. I got dressed and went into the kitchen to prepare dinner.

"Bryan, tomorrow me and my fucking kids are leaving. I will call my mom and have her wire me some money. You are not going to keep putting your hands on me." I said, slamming pots around in the kitchen.

"Go bitch! Nobody's making you stay."

Chapter 11
Back Home Again

I called my mother the next day to see about getting a little money so we could come home.

"Mom, can you send me some money? The kids and I are coming home, and I don't think I have enough for gas to get there."

"What's wrong, Rachel?"

"Bryan has been hitting me, Mom. I cannot do this anymore. He won't get help."

"I knew he was a sorry SOB. I don't have much money, but I will send what I can to Western Union. Go there in a few hours. When are you coming?"

"I am leaving today. I already have the car packed, and the kids and I are just sitting at the park until I can figure things out." I said as I began to cry.

The children played at the park until my mother could get money wired to me. I loaded the car with just the necessities for us to make our way back to Indiana. I did not have a plan for when we arrived. I just knew that I could not stay in that situation with Bryan. Nothing I did seemed to help. I thought my compassion and love would help him recover, but Bryan was unwilling to see a professional. I loved him, but my love wasn't enough, and I wasn't going to let him hit me.

I was hoping and praying all the way there that the car would make it. When we finally pulled into the driveway of my parents' home, I was relieved, tired, and broken.

It was the last place that I wanted to be, but I had few choices, so there I was once again in the same house with my abusive father, the man who stole my innocence, the man that I despised more than any other human being.

A few things had changed since our last time home. Matthew had married and moved to Arizona, my second brother was now in his teens, and my mother had given birth to another boy just two years before Adam was born. My two youngest brothers kept Adam pretty busy, but for Angel, I was doing my very best to keep her from the hands of my father. I never left Angel alone with my father. Every time I went somewhere, I made sure to take her with me. Sadly, I felt that if my mother could not protect me when I was a child, she indeed could not protect Angel. I was taking no chances.

Chance was thrilled to have his children back in Indiana, where he could see them regularly. By this time, he had re-married and had two stepsons. It had been a couple of years since he saw Adam and Angel. He was happy to know that they were within the same county, and they were safe.

With my instability and inability to provide at the time, Chance started fighting for custody of the children. Chance hired an attorney and took steps to fight me in court. He knew it would be a battle, but if he could prove the abuse that the children witnessed and the length of time I kept the children from him, he hoped he had a shot at least at joint custody.

Chance convinced me to let him have the children for a few weeks. By now, it was summertime, and he had already missed out on so much. I agreed.

What I did not agree to was him getting custody. When the few weeks were up, I contacted Chance inquiring about the return of the children. My calls went unanswered. I began to panic. I knew things were a mess in my personal life, but the children were my world, and I would not let another woman raise them.

Finally, I was able to get through to Chance, calling repeatedly and showing up at his work.

"Chance, I am picking the kids up today. Why haven't you answered or returned my calls? I have been worried, sick." I yelled into the phone.

"Rachel, I have hired an attorney; I am fighting for custody. These kids have been through too much. They need stability in their lives. You have been dragging them all over the fucking country, and they have witnessed things that most adults don't see in their lifetime. You need to get your shit together." Chance hung up the phone.

I sobbed as the phone went dead. "No! This isn't fucking right!" I screamed. My mother heard me screaming from the other room.

"Rachel, what is wrong?" Forcefully opening the door.

"Chance won't give the kids back; he is fighting me for custody. Mom, what am I going to do?"
My mother hugged me as she sat beside me on the twin bed in the boy's room. She grabbed the phone from my hand and put it back on the receiver.

"Come to the kitchen and get a piece of cake. I just made it earlier today."

"Mom, I don't feel like having cake right now. Why do you always insist on eating cake when things are falling apart?" I shook my head.

119

"Rachel, cake reminds me of life. See, you will go through some tough times, and you will have some wonderful times in this life. All those times make up what life is. Just like a cake. Flour, raw eggs, and oil, alone do not taste very good. Once you mix them, add some sugar, and bake it, it turns into this delicious cake. Our lives are not meant to be perfect, but all those moments, good and bad, can turn into something extraordinary. Plus, a cake is comforting when you are sad, and it is great when you are celebrating. When I do not have the words to say, a piece of cake shows that I care. This is one of those moments." My mother squeezed my hand as she explained herself and then guided me towards the kitchen.

My mother stayed in contact with Chance throughout the last couple of years. She was keeping him up to date on where the children and I were. She thought maybe she could talk to him. She felt compelled to call Chance the next day to plead with him over returning the children.

"Chance, it's Millie; Rachel told me you are trying to fight for custody. Please do not do this to her; you know she is a good mother. She has a job now and left Bryan. Ralph and I are trying to help her get back on her feet. The children need their mother; please don't do this." My mother pleaded.

"I will think about it, Millie. I want what is best for my kids. They do not deserve to live the way they have been living. I can give them a better life, Millie, some stability. Let me think about it. I will get back to you."

Tears filled my mother's eyes as she hung up the phone. She knew the only thing that kept me moving forward was my children. She did not know what would become of me if I lost them. Little did anyone know, but Chance's new wife did not want the children. As bad as Chance wanted to fight for custody of them, it was causing chaos in his own home. His wife did not want the responsibility of two more children, which was the first time they had them for more than a few hours. It would be a big adjustment. Chance did not know what to do.

"Hello! Millie, it is Chance. I am going to bring the kids back on one condition."

"Okay, what is that?"

"I want to know where my kids are living at all times, and Rachel doesn't leave this county with them without me knowing." Chance said sternly.

"Okay, Chance, Rachel is at work, but I am sure she will agree with you. Just bring them home."

Chance returned the children, and we resumed the standard visitations. When I did not let Chance know where we were living, my mother kept her promise and contacted him. Without my knowledge, the two of them had an understanding.

A massive thunderstorm had rolled in around 3 pm. Lightning was loudly cracking, lighting up the cloud covered sky. The rain beat against the windows, so loud and fierce, almost shaking the house. It was a typical summer storm in Indiana.

"Rachel, is someone knocking at the door?" My mother called out.

"No, Mom, that is just the storm."

"Are you sure? Go check. I am cutting potatoes for dinner." She yelled from the kitchen.

I put the clothes I was folding down in the basket and went to check, knowing it was just the storm. I looked out the window and did not see anything. As I turned back, I heard the knock. I opened the door. Standing there drenched in Army fatigues was Bryan.

"Hi! Can I come in? This storm is crazy."

I did not say a word as I opened the door for Bryan to come in.

"What are you doing here, Bryan?" I grabbed a towel from the hall closet and handed it to Bryan.

"I am out." Bryan began wiping himself down.

"You are out? What do you mean you are out?"

"I am out of the Army. They discharged me and put me on a bus two days ago. I wanted to come here, first, to see you and the kids. We can start over, make a new life. I think it will be better now. I am home, baby," Bryan said with excitement in his voice.

"Bryan, I don't know about that. You hurt me; I am not going back to that life with you."

"I know, babe, and I am so sorry. I am better now, really. I will never hurt you again. I love you and miss you and the kids so much. I want to hug you, but I am soaked." Bryan motioned to his drenched clothing.

"Dad!" Angel hesitantly said as she came from the other room. The children began calling Bryan dad when they moved away from Chance.

"Hi, sissy! Man, have I missed you. Daddy is all wet, or else I would hug you." Bryan kneeled to Angel's level.

"That's okay. I missed you too." Angel hugged Bryan anyway.

"Angel, go in the other room. Daddy and I need to talk." I said softly to Angel.

"Bryan, you can't stay here. My parents know what happened in Kansas and Colorado. I don't think they will want you here."

"That's cool. Hey man, I get it. I was a bad guy, but I have changed. Can I use the phone to call my dad to pick me up?"

"Sure." I walked with Bryan into the kitchen to use the phone. My mother turned away from peeling potatoes; disbelief came over her face.

"Mom, Bryan is going to use the phone to call his dad to pick him up. He isn't staying."

"Hi Millie, how are you?" Bryan said as if he was glad to see her.

"I am good, Bryan. You know where the phone is."

My mother pointed in the direction of the phone stand with her knife in her hand. That phone stand had been in the same place for years. A coffee cup held an array of pens and pencils, while the shelf underneath the stand housed the local phone directory and my mother's address book with all her friends' and family's contact information. The "R" page was full of all the places I had lived. Each one scratched out, replacing the next. She ran out of pages, so my list overflowed into the "S" page.

I was working trying to save money for a place of my own, away from my father. Bryan, showing up, threw a wrench in my plans. I was not ready.

Bryan's father picked him up a short while later.

We made small talk before he arrived, not discussing any of the previous events that led up to me leaving. I did not know what to think about Bryan's return, I still loved him, but I was determined to not live with the abuse. I was not going to risk losing my kids either. I had some decisions to make.

Chapter 12
Broken Promises

"Rachel, what on earth are you doing? You are not going back to that loser, are you? Christ sakes, Rachel, the children are calling him Dad? Have you lost your damn mind?" My mother yelled as she finished making dinner.

"No, Mom, I am not going back to him. I did not know he was going to show up here. The kids wanted to call him Dad. Bryan has been good to them."

"They are too young to know what they want. Good to them? Beating their mother is good to them?"

"Mom, stop! I am not going back to him. Let's drop it." I walked out of the room.

Bryan was attentive to the children. He played with them, taught them things, and when things were good between him and me, they were good. My love for Bryan was more substantial than I had ever known. He was affectionate and gentle. Most of the time, he was kind and made me feel loved. It was the moments when he lost control that I could not bear. I was torn between the love I had for him and the abuse I took.

Maybe he had changed, I thought. Perhaps he was better, and we could start over. Maybe time apart made him realize how much he loved me.

Going against what everyone thought I should do, I reached out to Bryan. I stopped by his parent's home several times, trying to get a feel for what our future might hold.

"It's so good to see you, Rach. Can you bring the kids over? I miss them like crazy. Mom and Dad want to see them too." Bryan grabbed my hand as we sat at the kitchen table drinking coffee.

"I could probably do that. I am sure the kids would be glad to see you too." I smiled.

Without anyone's knowledge, the children and I began spending time with Bryan at his parents' home. Things were great. Things were the way they were before the tragedy that took place in Kansas. I could see things working out for us. Maybe we could start a new life. Maybe this time it would be better.

Slowly I began putting things in place to move out of my parent's home and starting over again with Bryan. I secured a small farmhouse on the outskirts of town. The rent was cheap, and it would give Bryan and me enough privacy to work on our issues. Bryan loved the outdoors, and I hoped that he would find peace there. I hoped that moving away from Kansas, getting out of the military, and having room to breathe might help him work through Tank's death. Bring back the Bryan I once knew.

I kept my plans to myself, slowly moving into that small farmhouse, painting the children's rooms their favorite colors. Adam's bedroom was blue, and Angel's bright pink. A small apple orchard behind the house supplied us with an abundance of fresh apples, and Angel had all the kittens she could ever want. The bus picked the children up at the end of the driveway for school every morning, and the endless dirt piles and country roads were a haven for Adam and his toys. The children were thrilled, and so was I. Things seemed normal again.

"Hey babe, I got a gig playing at the Foust House on Saturday's. I am pretty excited about it. Some of the old band members are getting back together. Mom and Dad said they would watch the kids. It will be like the old times." Bryan kept rambling on with excitement in his voice.

"Oh, that is good. I would love to hear you play again. You are a talented musician. Sounds like fun." I did not want to admit it, but the times Bryan and I spent in those smoke-filled dive bars were some of our best and worst times.

Bryan's dream of becoming a super-star musician continued to get in the way of him securing full-time employment. He made music his priority. I continued to foot the bill.

As winter set in, the farmhouse was becoming difficult to heat. A wood-burning stove sat in the middle of the living room floor. Fuel oil was getting expensive, so we started cutting wood to feed the stove to stay warm.

By now, everyone was aware, including Chance, that Bryan was back in the picture. Much to everyone's dislike, they said nothing.

Few words were spoken about his lack of contribution to our household, financially and otherwise. Instead of cutting wood for heat Bryan employed others to do it for him. Like always, it was my income that paid for it. Anytime I spoke about it, a fight would start. I avoided saying anything, hoping Bryan would realize that he needed to provide in some way. He did not.

Bryan continued to play music in the house band on the weekends. Bryan spent every penny he made on things he needed or wanted.

Nothing went towards our living expenses. I felt as if I had three children I was raising instead of two. I was frustrated. As much as I enjoyed watching Bryan play music, I would not go on the weekends I had the children. I needed to spend time with them, so I did.

Bryan would be gone until all hours of the morning. I worried every time he did not come home at his usual hour. Filled with jealousy, I worried that he would meet someone else; someone younger, someone thinner, more attractive, or someone without children.

"Where the hell have you been, Bryan?" I asked as Bryan came strolling in the door.

"What do you mean, where have I been? You are not my mother. I was working," Bryan said as he put his guitar case down.

"Your set was over at 1 am. It is now 1 pm the next day. Where did you stay? Who are you sleeping with, Bryan? Some random girl you met in the bar?" I kept on.

"I stayed at my parent's. I had a few drinks, and I didn't want to drive home. Call them if you don't believe me. But don't ever fucking accuse me of sleeping around." Bryan replied, pointing his finger at me.

"It is a little hard to call them when we don't have a phone. We can't afford a phone because you won't get a job."

"Oh, okay. I told you I was looking for one. Leave me alone I am going to go lay down. I am exhausted. Playing music is my job." Bryan went into the bedroom to lay down.

I followed him as I continued yelling. I stood on the bed, straddled over Bryan, preventing him from sleeping.

"You're exhausted? Playing in a house band is not a job, Bryan. It is a fucking hobby. Job's pay bills. Your so-called job doesn't pay for shit."

"I said, leave me the fuck alone. Rachel, I am warning you. You better leave me alone."

"Or what? You going to call your girlfriend and have her whoop my ass? Or better yet, get your mommy and daddy to bail you out because that is what they always do?

Bryan jumped up from the laying position, grabbed me by the throat, and shoved me into the bedroom wall. Bryan's force was so strong that I was stuck inside the wall. Drywall went flying as the wall broke into pieces.

"I told you to leave me alone. See what you made me do." Bryan got into the car and drove off.

I managed to free myself from the wall after I called for the children to help me.

"Mommy, what happened?" Adam asked.

"I fell into the wall. I am okay. Here grab mommy's hand and pull."

Adam and Angel manage to pull me loose. As I fell onto the bed, we all started to laugh. The children did not understand how, but they believed that I fell into the wall. I never told them any different, even though they might have known, but they did not say either way. I am sure they heard Bryan and me fighting before it happened.

Bryan left with the only vehicle we owned. We had no phone, no food, and no wood for the wood-burning stove. It was the dead of winter, and the snow was accumulating fast as a winter storm set in.

"Adam, get your boots, coat, hat, and gloves on. We are going to have to see if we can find some wood. Angel, you stay here. You are too little."

Adam and I bundled up to go outside and face the winter storm, searching for any wood we could find for heat. Returning with mostly twigs, we managed to keep a small fire going. That evening we brought a mattress into the front room to sleep on by the wood-burning stove. Huddled up with several blankets, we tried to stay warm.

The next day I dressed Angel in her winter clothes, and we headed down the road for two miles in a foot of snow until we reached the corner store. The store offered a variety of items. I had been in there before to grab a last-minute dinner item.

We shook off the cold as the brass bell on the door chimed. Stomping the snow from our feet, we were greeted by a middle-aged lady dressed in a festive, outdated sweater.

"Hello! How can I help you?" The lady charmingly said.

"Ma'am, my kids and I live in the old Palmer farmhouse up the road. My husband left us a couple of days ago, and we don't have any food." I said humbly.

"Well, I have a few things here. There is soup over there and a few boxes of cereal. What are you looking for?"

"No, I don't think you understand. I do not have any money. Can you help us?" Holding Angel's hand, I began to cry.

"I understand, but this isn't a charity. This store is our business and how we make a living. I can't just give my stuff to you." The store clerk said sternly.

130

"I will come back and pay you for everything. I work, but I don't have any money right now. Ma'am, please. If you don't help us, we are going to starve." Humbly, I began to beg. I looked down at Angel as if to get a glimpse of sympathy from the clerk. I was embarrassed and ashamed for both of us, but I was desperate.

"I don't know. If I do this for you, then everyone will think it is free for the taking. Let me get my husband."

The clerk went into the back room and spoke to her husband. I could hear her telling him everything I just said. Angel and I stood quietly still, waiting for the lady to return. I looked down, smiling at Angel, brushing her hair from her eyes. When I looked up from her, we saw this tall, heavy-set man in overalls, flannel shirt, and a long white beard come from around the corner. I was sure he was going to run us off. With the jolliest voice, the man knelt by Angel.

"Looks like you girls need some groceries. Wilma, go get these little angels a couple of paper bags." The man said, looking back at his wife.

"That's my name!" Angel said with a big smile.

"You know, I could have guessed that." The man pinched Angel's cheek.

"Fill those bags up, and don't forget to grab a couple of pieces of that bubble gum for you and your brother." The man winked at Angel and patted me on the shoulder before returning to the back room.

"Sir, I will pay you back, I promise. Thank you!" I said, relieved.

The man turned around and looked at me firmly in the eyes.

"No need, young lady. The good Lord has blessed me. Helping another in need is what he calls us to do. I suspect you will do the same for someone in the future."

Angel held the bags as I filled them with canned goods, a carton of eggs, and a few boxed goods. I was making sure not to make them too heavy for our journey back home.

"Thank you so much. You have no idea how much this has helped us." I said as Angel and I headed towards the door. Angel dropped my hand, turning to wave at the lady standing there with her hands on her hips.

"Bye, nice lady!"

Angel and I began walking the two miles back towards home, doing our best to keep a hold of the bags of food. I started crying during our walk. I was stressed, beaten down, and just plain worn out. I did not want this life for my children or me, but I didn't know how to get there from here.

"Don't cry, Mommy. It's going to be okay." Angel said, looking up at me, chewing her bubble gum.

Chapter 13
Somethings Never Change

The children and I managed to make it through the few days of cold and hunger pangs. Bryan came rolling in the driveway just as the snow began to melt. I was furious for many reasons, but I was relieved by his return. I was relieved that I could take the car into town and get the things that we needed.

I was also rethinking my decision to move into a hard-to-heat farmhouse secluded from everything. I could not believe I let Bryan back into our lives again. I was exhausted and fed up with supporting a grown man, fed up with worrying about whether he was faithful, and just plain fed up with life. But every time I got to the point of ending the roller coaster ride of a marriage, Bryan would sweep in with his manipulative kindness, his confession of his love, and reel me back in. The power he had over my emotions was unexplainable. Bryan could manipulate my thoughts so much I did not know if I believed them myself. He twisted things in a way that I began blaming myself for the abuse. I felt like I was losing my mind half the time.

When I was away from him, I could clearly see the situation I was in and that it needed to end. Things were not going to change, and neither was he. Once he stepped back into the picture, all the thoughts I had about ending it were exchanged with thoughts of guilt and shame.

"What, you aren't speaking to me?" Bryan asked as he put his bag by the door.

"You have been gone for a week. You left the kids and me here with no food, no heat, and no car while you were out having a hell of a time. So no, I don't really have anything to say to you." I replied, throwing a hand towel down on the sink.

"I told you to leave me alone, Rachel. You just kept on and kept on. You know I can't deal with someone in my face, especially after what happened to Tank. You should have just left me alone, and none of this would have happened".

"Oh, so it's my fault that you pushed me through a wall?"

"You won't quit. You will not just let me be. Maybe it is your fault because you back me into a corner until I explode. Rachel, you know I don't want to hurt you. I love you. You know I don't like getting to that point, and I don't like fighting with you. You are my love, my everything, and I miss you so much when we aren't together. Come on, babe, you know that is not me. I just love you so much that I don't know what comes over me." Bryan grabbed my hand as I swiftly pulled away.

"Where have you been, Bryan?"

"At Mom and Dads. Just trying to put some distance between us so we could both cool off. Come here and kiss me. I missed you." Bryan tried pulling me close to him again.

I was still mad, but Bryan could always sweet talk his way back. It was those moments that kept me going back to him. Bryan always knew what to say to get me to give in. After an explosive fight, we would reunite with more passion than before. Each time it was like the first time. Almost like chasing a drug, I found myself always trying to get back to that feeling I first felt with Bryan.

134

When we made up after a big fight, I got that feeling again. I began looking forward to it. I did not like the fighting part, but I looked forward to the making up part. There was no spark without the fighting, and without that spark, there wasn't the passion. It was an endless cycle.

As much as Bryan hated it, he went to work with his father working on old coal and fuel oil furnaces, hoping to make me happy. He kept his music gig on the weekends, still trying to pursue his dream.

Life was somewhat normal for us again, for the moment. We were both working, and the kids were in school. Chance was paying child support and picking them up for visitations. Things were getting better, but things never stayed that way for long for the two of us.

Bryan refused to let go of his music dream. He loved the feeling he got being on stage, people giving him praise after he played, and the women dancing in front of him trying to get his attention. It was more than just music. It was the atmosphere. No matter what I did or said, I could not convince him to give it up and live an everyday life.

My continued jealousy over Bryan kept me from going to watch him play on my weekends without the children. Bryan encouraged me to stay home, which fueled my jealousy even further, causing numerous fights over who this was and why they were talking to him. It was constant.

On Friday, the children were staying at Bryan's parents while I was at work. When I stopped by to pick them up, I ran into Bryan's sister, Karen. Karen and I had become good friends over the years. We were the same age, and our kids were close in age too.

"Hey Rachel, let's go down to the Foust House and watch Bryan play tonight. Mom and Dad will keep all the kids. I could use a night out. What about you?" Karen asked.

"I could use a little fun. You know Bryan doesn't want me there, but if your Mom and Dad don't mind keeping all of the kids, I guess I will go. I will need to borrow some makeup. I am not running all the way home."

"I already asked Mom and Dad, and of course, you can use whatever you need. Don't worry about Bryan; you are with me." Karen grabbed my arm, pulling me into the bathroom. "Let's get ready."

The two of us dolled up and smoked a couple of joints before heading off to the bar. As we walked through the front door, the band was on their break. Immediately I looked over to see Bryan sitting with a couple of band members and several women. I was furious.

"What are you two doing here?" Bryan said, looking up from the table.

"We came to watch my baby brother do his thing," Karen said as she patted Bryan on the back.

"Well, sit down, I guess." Bryan pulled out a chair.

"You guess?"

"Don't start, Rachel." Bryan got up and headed towards the stage.

"Come on, girl, we are going to have a good time. It would help if you lightened up. Let me get some drinks." Karen went to the bar and bought our first round of drinks.

Karen and I stayed all night, dancing, drinking, and talking with old friends. Bryan did not say a whole lot to me. He was not happy about me showing up unannounced. In recent months Bryan discouraged me from coming to watch him play. Each time I did, there was always a fight. Bryan did not like having to answer for every woman he spoke to or every moment that I couldn't see him. Groupies were part of it, and I just needed to get over it.

I was so insecure about our relationship. I did not trust the other women, and I wasn't sure how much I trusted Bryan. As far as I knew, Bryan had never been unfaithful, but I knew how easily an affair could happen in a place like a bar. I also knew that musicians always seemed to catch other women's eye, regardless of whether they were married, and I knew that was exactly how I met Bryan.

The night went off without incident. I refrained from asking questions, probably more so because I was drunk and having a good time myself. Bryan managed to get me home, leaving the children with his parents for the night. Although I was extremely intoxicated, the two of us engaged in intercourse that evening. Bryan was just happy we were not fighting and having to explain himself.

The next afternoon I forced myself to get out of bed. I was terribly hungover. Trying to get woke up, I stumbled to the bathroom, thinking a shower could help. As I sat down on the toilet, I looked down to see tiny little bugs jumping all over my pubic area.

"You have got to be fucking kidding me," I shouted.

"Bryan, get in here."

Bryan opened the door, thinking I was hurt.

"What's wrong?"

"You gave me fucking crabs, Bryan. That is what's wrong." I grabbed Bryan's underwear and began tugging at them to pull them down. "See, you fucking have them too. You are a piece of shit. Who have you been sleeping with?" I stood up and grabbed the clippers from under the sink. As I began shaving all my pubic hair off, I continued yelling at Bryan.

"Answer me, Bryan. Who is she? Or are there multiple ones? Answer me."

"I haven't been with anyone. You probably got crabs from the bathroom last night and gave them to me." Bryan said as he grabbed the clippers to shave his pubic area.

"Really? From the bathroom? If I got them from the bathroom, then your sister has them too cause we went to the bathroom together. I guess I will find out when I go pick up the kids today."

A few hours later, after I took a shower and cleaned up the hair mess from the bathroom, I jumped into the car and went to Bryan's parents to pick up the children. Karen did not have the crabs, which solidified my suspicions. He cheated. Not only did he cheat, but he brought home crabs. I was disgusted and angry.

I could not wait to confront Bryan when I got home. As soon as I walked into the house, I started in on him.

"Your sister doesn't have crabs. Now, do you want to tell me who she is? Do I need to go to the bar and start asking questions?" I kept yelling louder and louder.

138

"You better not even think about going to my place of work. I told you, I am not sleeping with anyone. I do not know where the crabs came from, and I am not fighting with you, Rachel. I am leaving."

"Not in my car, you're not. You are not leaving us stranded again. You just proved your guilt. So fucking leave, but you will be walking this time." I grabbed Bryan's bag and threw it out the door. "While you are at it, take all of your shit." I started grabbing drawers full of clothes, throwing them on the front lawn. I reached for Bryan's guitar when he grabbed my arm and pushed me down.

"You better not touch my guitar, bitch." Bryan turned to walk away when I got up and grabbed the back of his shirt, pulling him towards me. Bryan got up, turned, and punched me square in the nose. I fell back into the couch, but I got up and lunged towards him. Bryan hit me again. This time I fell to the floor. Bryan straddled me, punching me in the face and the chest repeatedly. He hit me in the ribs when I tried to cover my face to protect myself from the blows. The door swung open.

"Daddy, stop it, stop it." The children were crying as they stood back and screamed.

Bryan snapped out of it, grabbed his bag, and took off walking down the road. My face was black and blue, my nose was broken, and my eyes and lips were swollen. This was the worst beating yet.

The children ran to my aid, helping me up off the floor. Angel went into the kitchen and got ice and a washcloth from the hall closet, helping me clean up.

"Mommy, we need to leave. You need to go to the hospital." Adam said, frightened.

"It is okay, sweetie. I am fine. I need to clean up. Let Mommy go take a bath."

I went into the bathroom and got a glimpse of myself in the mirror. Oh, my God. I looked like the elephant man, and I was horrified at the sight of my mangled face. I attempted to take a shower, but I could barely see as my eyes began to swell shut. My loose teeth hid behind my swollen lips. I was a mess, and there was no way of hiding this one.

It was bad.

Chapter 14
It's Time to Go

Adam ran to the neighbor's house and called my mother while I was in the shower, concerned for me, for us.

"Grandma, my Mom, needs to go to the hospital, but she won't go," Adam said as soon as my mother picked up the phone.

"What's wrong with her?"

"Dad beat her up really bad. It is really bad, this time. Will you come to get me?"

"Dad? You mean Bryan?"

"Yes, he beat her up really bad."

"I am on my way. I will be there shortly. Do not let him back in that house, Adam. You run to a neighbor and call 911 if he comes back." My mother hung up the phone, clutched her purse under her arm, and flew out the door.

I had no idea that Adam had called her. I was in a lot of pain but going to the hospital was not an option. The hospital asked too many questions, and they could not do any more than I was doing to treat my injuries. Plus, I was not going to risk them taking Adam and Angel.

As always, I needed to pull myself together. My children needed me, and I did not want to let them down.

My mother showed up just as I was getting out of the shower.

"Oh my God, Rachel! He really did a number on you this time. When are you going to get rid of him for good?"

"Not now, Mom. The last thing I need is for you to tell me how stupid I am for taking him back. It is over. I am leaving him for good this time." I said as I stood wrapped in a towel, holding ice to my face. "I need to get the fuck out of this place. Away from Bryan, away from everything. A new start." I broke down crying.

"Why don't you talk to Matthew? Maybe he can help you, and the kids get on your feet. Have you tried calling him?"

"Mom, I haven't been in the mood to call anyone. I mean, this just happened a few hours ago. He was not the first person I thought about calling. Plus, what about Chance? He is not going to go for me leaving again. I surely can't let him see me like this. He is liable to kill Bryan."

"Maybe that's not a bad thing."

"Mom!"

My mother took Adam home with her. Angel stayed behind with me and helped mend my wounds. When my mother got home, she called my brother Matthew in Arizona and explained the situation. He agreed to help me and the children get on our feet. Jobs were plentiful out there, so I would have no problem finding a job.

Even though Matthew's wife was pregnant, she was not due for several months. They had plenty of time to help me find a place of our own. Everyone wanted me away from Bryan. They knew it was no kind of life for my children or me. They wanted to help; however, they could.

I only had a few days to gather our belongings before my mother put the children and me on a Grey Hound bus to Arizona. I left behind everything but our clothes.

We loaded up snacks, pillows, and small blankets for the two and ½ day road trip. Those buses were always cold, and I could not afford the food along the way. We needed to make do.

Before we left, I gathered everything Bryan left behind and set fire to it. It was closure for me. I thought it would help me move on, help me realize it was over. Close a chapter.

My attempt at hiding did not work that well. It was obvious what I was leaving behind as I wore sunglasses the whole time, even at night, trying to hide my bruised and battered face. Heartache, broken promises, love lost, and shame surrounded me. People on the bus and at the bus stations looked at me with pity. Two children in tow to an unknown place, no money, and a broken heart. I was beaten on the outside, but I was beaten and defeated on the inside, too.

Arriving at Matthews after the long bus ride, the children and I were dirty and tired.

"Come on, Sis; it's time to get up, brush yourself off, and start over. We will help you. There are plenty of jobs here. It should not take long to get one. For now, go shower and get the kids ready for bed." Matthew said, trying to encourage me as he showed me where we would be sleeping.

I took some time finding a job. Obviously, I could not go job hunting with the shape my face was in. Matthew took me to see his doctor so we could see if they could set my nose, but too much time had passed, and the break was not severe enough. They decided to let it be. I now have a slight crook in my nose, a constant reminder of the beating I took that day.

143

I found an office job down the street from Matthew's place. Matthew dropped me off at work and picked me up on his way home every day. The school was a couple of blocks over, so Adam and Angel could walk to school.

I saved as much money as I could for a place of my own. Matthew and his wife were generous but living with someone else, sleeping on the floor in sleeping bags was not ideal. We needed our own space, and the children needed their own room. I had no privacy and no life.

Once the bruises healed, I found myself missing Bryan deeply. I called his mom and dad several times, trying to reach him, talking to him periodically throughout the six months, and of course, hiding my phone calls from everyone, only calling him from work.

As always, Bryan confessed his love and regret. He told me how sorry he was for what he did, saying it would never happen again. I reluctantly believed everything Bryan said. He always knew the right words to say to get me to give in. Partially blaming it on me, but he would take the blame and seem genuinely regretful. Our phone conversations increased and resembled the same discussions we had when I was married to Chance. It was like we were having an emotional affair all over again. Bryan remained calm and kind while speaking with me over the phone. It was easy for me to be sucked in when I did not know what he was doing or who he was doing it with. He told me everything I wanted to hear.

After about six months, I was able to secure an apartment not far from Matthew's. The children could stay in the same school, where they could walk back and forth.

Matthew helped me buy a car, an old 1964 light blue Rambler he purchased from a neighbor. The seats were torn, the headliner was falling in, there was no A/C, and did not need a key to start. It was not much, but it was getting me where I needed to go.

The children and I settled into our apartment, shopping at yard sales every weekend, trying to find things to furnish our new place. Fortunately, the small apartment came with most of the big furniture, but we needed some things like dishes and pots and pans since we left everything we owned in Indiana.

Our lives were moving on, but I failed to tell Chance where we were living again. I broke the promise I made to him, and for the past six months, he had been worried sick about where we were and our wellbeing. Once he was able to get my work phone number from my mother, he made the call.

"Rachel speaking."

"Rachel, it's Chance. Why did you take my kids again? You didn't even give me a chance to say goodbye. You promised you would not do this to me. You can't keep dragging them all over the place, and you can't keep taking them from me."

"I am sorry, Chance, but we had to get out of there in a hurry. In a matter of days, we were on a bus headed out here to Matthew's. I didn't have time to think. I just knew we needed to leave. I can't talk right now, Chance. I am at work."

"Please let the kids call me. They need to know I love them. Please, Rachel!"

"As soon as we get a phone, I will have them call. I have to go, take care, Chance."

145

I knew it was hurting him, so I did as I said I would, and once I got us a phone, I allowed the children to call him as much as I could. The long-distance calls were expensive, encouraging Chance to call instead.

"Hello!"
"Who is this? Chance asks.
"It's Bryan. Who is this?"
"This is Chance. Are the kids around?"
"Just a minute."

Chance tried to hold back his anger as he realized Bryan was back in the picture. I was 2000 miles from Indiana, and Bryan somehow found his way there. Chance was furious. This loser was seeing his children more than he was. Subjecting them to drugs, alcohol, and abuse, but there was nothing he could do. He was so angry with me, and for the life of him, could not figure out what I was thinking, letting this guy back into our lives.

"Hi, Daddy!" Angel answers.
"Hi baby girl, how was school today?"
"It was good. I fell and cut my knee when I was roller skating." Angel goes on, telling Chance all about her new adventures.
"Is Adam home? I want to say hello to him too."
"No, he is at his friend's house playing race cars or something. I have to go, Daddy, my friend, is here, and she brought Barbie's. Love you."
Angel hung up the phone.

Chance knew there was nothing he could say to me that would make me change my mind about Bryan.
Something about Bryan kept me hanging on, something that I never felt for Chance. At this point, all he wanted was to see his children.

Chapter 15
Life Will Go On

I tried to hide the fact that Bryan was back in our lives as much as possible, but it did not take long for my family or Chance to find out.

Things were fantastic between us, just like they always were after a separation. Bryan was kind, gentle, and romantic. We were in the honeymoon stage again, but it would only take one thing to start a big fight, and we both knew it. So, we refrained from saying anything or doing anything that would cause friction. We were trying to make it work this time.

Bryan was able to find work but regularly working never lasted long for him. He could not seem to get up on time to get ready for a day job, and a night job interfered with his music. He would keep a job for a few weeks and then find a reason to quit or get fired because of performance and tardiness.

Once again, I found myself being the provider while Bryan messed around all day smoking pot and playing music. It was a constant battle, and I did not know how to change it, nagging him all the time about working was getting old. When would I learn that this man was never going to change?

As much as I wanted it to work out between us, I was tired of holding my tongue and tired of struggling to make ends meet with a grown man living in my home. I was again was about to lose my cool when I received a phone call. It was early afternoon on April 15th, 1981.

"Rachel speaking!"

"Rachel, it's Mom. I need to talk to you. Do you have a minute?" My mother's voice was trembling.

"What's wrong, Mom? Are you ok? Tell me."

My mother took a deep breath and swallowed the lump in her throat.

"There has been an accident, and Chance is dead. Bryan's mother called me this morning and wanted to make sure you and the kids knew. I heard it on the radio, but they had the name wrong, so I didn't think much of it."

The phone went silent as I sat there in shock as the words sank in. Chance is dead.

"Rachel, are you there?"

"I am here, Mom. What happened?"

"He was shot accidentally in the stomach. They said suicide, but I don't believe that."

"No! No! Chance would never kill himself." My voice trembled as I tried holding the phone in one hand and my face in the other. I was overcome with guilt, knowing he was devastated about me taking the children. Could he have possibly killed himself because of what I had done?

"His brother Tom said he thought his step-son killed him. He is only 14 years old, though. I don't know Rachel. Do you want me to try to figure out how to get the kids back here for the funeral?"

"I will figure something out, Mom, but I don't think we can get enough money up in a couple of days. I am broke, and Bryan isn't working."

"Well, of course, he's not. He is never going to be a provider, Rachel. You need to get rid of his ass for good."

"Ok, Mom. I will call you tomorrow. I need to figure out how to tell the kids."

149

I spoke to my boss, and of course, he was more than generous about me leaving early to handle the situation. Before I left work, I called Bryan to tell him what happened and that I was on my way home.

"Hello!"

"Hey Bryan, it's me. I have some terrible news."

"Oh no, babe, what's wrong?"

"Chance has been killed. I just got off the phone with Mom. I don't know how I am going to tell the kids. I am getting ready to leave work. I will be home shortly."

I held back my heartbreak, not wanting Bryan to know how much it hurt me to hear of Chance's passing. He was always jealous of Chance, and I am sure his death would not have changed that.

"Ok honey, I will call for the children. They are outside playing right now. Be careful. We will see you in a few."

Bryan called the children inside to wait for me. Now eleven years old, Adam was riding his bike, and Angel, now nine years old, was playing Barbie's with a neighbor. They were both anxious to know what was going on to resume what they were doing outside. Changes were not unusual for the children; they had become accustomed to it. The only difference was that most of the time, I gave them no forewarning. They anticipated another move or a breakup between Bryan and me.

Before I got home, the children kept asking Bryan why they needed to talk. So, Bryan blurted it out.

"There's been an accident, and your real dad has been killed. I am so sorry, kiddos."

Real dad is how we referred to Chance in Bryan's presence. He knew he would never be the man Chance was, which made him extremely uneasy about his role in the children's lives.

Both children just sat there in shock. Angel began sobbing, but Adam only teared up. Chance always gave Angel special treatment. She was close to Chance and had always been a daddy's girl. Adam was indifferent about his dad. When he was little, Chance was hard on him and having two older stepbrothers didn't help matters, either. Chance never treated Adam the same way he did Angel. He was tender-hearted, but Chance wanted him to toughen up. After all, Chance was a Marine, and he was not going to have a sissy of a son.

Once I did arrive home, Adam was already back outside, riding his bike. Angel, however, stayed in her room for several hours by herself. She was the most affected by the news, even though it would be years later before she would understand the actual loss of her father's death.

Escaping into her room for hours, Angel used her Barbie's to role play, pretending that she was a part of a family where the dad did not beat the mom, where the mom didn't always cry from stress and heartache. A family that stayed in one place so she could keep her friends. A family that did not go hungry or without electricity. Escaping from the images in her mind of those dreaded beatings her mom took and the sheer fear as she watched without being able to help—the pictures in her mind of a dying man on their kitchen floor, shot by her stepdad. The heartbreak of losing her daddy, never knowing what it would be like to have him in her life as she grew into a woman.

All the things that she was never allowed to talk about, all the things that kept her awake at night, but she could never say. Angel felt everything. Every hurt from those closest to her resonated in her soul as if they happened directly to her. She felt their sorrow, their pain, never being able to distinguish between theirs and her own.

  In the quiet of her room with those dolls, Angel could live whatever life her little mind could imagine, and that was how she survived.

  Adam never spoke about Chance. He buried every feeling he had about Chance's death and everything that happened over the year's He was able to push it down and never let it resurface. His mind was able to block out most of the things he saw, that too, was how he survived. Life went on.

Chapter 16
A Ghostly Encounter

Angel was nine years old when her father passed away. By this time, she had experienced sorrow and death. She witnessed physical abuse, drug and alcohol abuse, and the constant moving that always kept us in turmoil.

Angel had a vivid imagination, one that she escaped to many times. So much so that I worried about the numerous hours she spent alone in her bedroom. Life never felt safe for her. At any moment, a fight could break out, and she and Adam would be picking up the pieces from whatever happened. From day to day, they did not know if it could be the last day. The last day to see their friends, to live in that place, or the last day they would see one of their parents.

Once the initial shock of Chance's passing faded, it was never spoken about. Like Tanks' death and everything else in our lives, it happened; we moved on and forgot about it. We never talked about any of it.

Angel could not forget about it, or any other things that were so vivid in her mind. She was a child, and she was not equipped to get over it. She needed something, she needed someone to talk to, but that never happened.

I did not realize then how much my children suffered silently. I was so consumed with my own life that I did not even know I was damaging theirs. I think Angel was affected the most because of what she remembered. Adam seemed able to block most of it from his mind, but Angel remembered every detail.

Just like my own mother, I never sought help for my children. I guess I, too, figured they would forget and move on with their own lives someday.

The small room that Adam and Angel shared had clunky wood twin beds with a matching nightstand in-between and a dresser against the opposite wall. Adam was a hard sleeper, but Angel laid awake many nights with her mind racing. Even at a young age, she was consumed by her thoughts.

One night laying in her bed half asleep, Angel awoke to an image. The image stood by the dresser, plain as day. It was the image of her father, a ghost-like figure standing there with a big smile.

Angel raised herself slowly from her bed, frightened by what she saw until he spoke. The image of what appeared to be her father spoke with a soft, gentle voice, his strawberry blonde hair and piercing blue eyes looking directly at her.

"Hi, baby girl. Daddy loves you, and everything is going to be okay. Don't you worry, I will always be with you."

As fast as the image came, it disappeared. Angel wiped the sleep from her eyes and stared at the dresser for hours, waiting for the image to return. Unsure if it was just a dream, nonetheless, she was holding onto the one last encounter with her father, even if it was just her imagination.

Angel never spoke to anyone about what she saw until many years later. It could have been just a dream, and she was sure no one wanted to hear about it.

She clung to that night in the back of her mind for the rest of her childhood. Those words that her father's image spoke to her gave her a sense of comfort.

"I will always be with you."

Angel believed that no matter where we lived or what things she endured, her father was always with her.
I had visions of my father too. The dreams I had were filled with the constant abuse I received as a child. I understood Angel's visions, even though mine were not as pleasant. It was easy to feel as if those visions were real. They were so vivid and carried so much detail that it was like it was happening all over again. I was happy that what little memory she had of her father was pleasant because mine was not.

Chapter 17
The Outside Looking In

Chance's death provided me with Social Security benefits for the children. The check I received monthly was a great deal more than I received in child support. The extra money provided a better way of life for us. But what it also provided was Bryan an excuse to continue to avoid getting a real job. We were not as strapped as we once were when the only income we had was mine. So, Bryan began to focus more on playing music again instead of getting a job. The source of most of our fights, Bryan could not let go of his dream.

I felt it was more important than ever to have Bryan in mine and the children's lives. They just lost Chance, and Bryan would be the only father they would have. I felt I had to make it work. I needed it to work for them and me.

I did my best to support Bryan's dream. I did believe that he was talented enough to make it big someday. When that time came, I hoped that he would look back on all that I endured and all the sacrifices I made and, maybe he would finally give me the life we both dreamed of.

With the additional income, I secured a three-bedroom home on the outskirts of town in a family-oriented neighborhood with good schools. It was the nicest place we had ever lived.

It looked like the perfect family, a lovely home, mom, dad, and two children. We even got a dog named Max, a massive male black Lab.

However, the chaos continued as Bryan and I constantly fought on the inside of that beautiful brick ranch home.

As much as I was jealous of Bryan, Bryan had that same jealousy for me. Neither of us trusted each other for whatever reason.

Out of the blue, Bryan showed up at my work. I was working as a secretary in a large plant close to where we lived. I loved my job, and my peers and my bosses highly respected me. I felt a sense of accomplishment in working there. He needed money for cigarettes, and I had all the money. As Bryan walked through the door, he saw me speaking to a tall, dark-haired, handsome man.

"I will get this taken care of right away. Thank you, John." Like always, I flashed a big smile at John. I was happy to help. I quickly turned to see Bryan walking through the door.

"Hey, what are you doing here?"

"What are you doing, and who is that?" Bryan's face turned red with anger.

"Who, John? He is my co-worker Bryan. I am working."

"You seemed awful friendly with him. Why are you calling him by his first name? Is there something going on between you two?"

"Bryan, nothing is going on between us. I am doing my job. Now, why are you here?"

"I need some money for cigarettes. You took all the money."

"Here, now you need to leave, or you are going to get me in trouble." I pulled 10 dollars out of my purse and handed it to Bryan.

Bryan grabbed the money forcefully.

"We will discuss this later."

I finished my day and thought nothing more about Bryan's jealousy. I was doing what I had to do to provide since he never seemed to be able to.

  As soon as I entered the door from work, Bryan starts in on me. He had been stewing all day about the guy I was talking to at work, my co-worker. Bryan's lack of abilities caused him a great deal of insecurity. He was not a provider, and he knew it. Deep down, he knew he brought nothing to the table. I always worked, and I was now getting $800 a month in social security for the children. In reality, Bryan offered nothing. I could make it without him, and probably better. I did not need him, and he knew it.

  "Rachel, you are going to tell me what you think you are doing, calling this man "John" by his first name. If he is your co-worker, shouldn't you be addressing him more professionally?"
  "Bryan, you obviously have no clue about the business world. But why would you? When was the last time you had a real job? You don't have any idea what you are talking about." I took off my shoes and headed to the kitchen to start dinner. "Bryan, you can't even start a meal for us. I do it all."
  "I know when something is going on between two people. There is something between you two, Rachel. I could see it." Bryan followed me into the kitchen, ranting about John.
  "Bryan, this is ridiculous. I am not having this conversation. Nothing is going on. Now drop it."
  "You are probably right. Who would want your hog headed, fat ass? You disgust me, so why would anyone else want you. I don't even know why I am with you."

"Fuck you, you mother fucker. I am done with you calling me names. Get your shit and go if you don't want to be here. I don't need you." I turned and threw the plate I was holding at Bryan. Bryan dodged the plate and then quickly walked over to me and grabbed me by the throat, pushing me against the refrigerator.

"Get your fucking hands off me." I tried to fight back, but Bryan only squeezed harder. "I can't breathe." I gasped for air. Bryan let loose of my throat and walked away. I caught my breath and was filled with anger. All I did wrong was go to work and speak to a man like I always did. I did not deserve to be spoken to or treated this way. I was so angry and fed up that I grabbed Bryan's guitar by the neck, his most prized possession, and slung it against the kitchen bar. Pieces went flying everywhere. I knew where to hit him where it hurt. He cared more about that guitar than anything else. Bryan quickly turned to see what I did. Furious, he lunged at me, and then we began to tussle. Bryan punched me in the face, again and again; I put my arms up, trying to protect myself.

Angel was walking home when she heard the commotion. She stopped a few houses down, knowing it was another big fight. Our fights were loud enough to be heard from down the street, and Angel recognized the yelling. In that neighborhood, you rarely heard any disturbances. She knew it was coming from her house, and she knew exactly what she was walking into. She braced herself.

Angel opened the door to find me on the floor in a cradled position trying to protect my head as Bryan kicked me repeatedly.

Angel grabbed Bryan's arm.

"Dad, stop! stop!"

Bryan forcefully pushed Angel, slamming her into the wall.

Angel got up and ran to her room, closed the door, and began to cry. She turned up her radio to drown out the yelling as the fight continued. Sobbing, Angel decided to go for help. She was too little to help me, but she knew someone needed to stop it. Angel crawled out her bedroom window and ran across the street to the neighbors. I walked up behind her just as she began to tell the neighbor what was going on.

"Angel, what are you doing?" I stood there with finger marks around my neck and blood coming from my nose. I did not have time to try to clean up before I realized she was gone. I had to stop her and apologize for Bryan pushing her. He did not touch the children. I knew she was scared.

"We are calling the police. Daddy was beating you up." Angel explained as she looked at me with the neighbor standing there in shock.

"No, no, don't do that. It is okay. We had a little fight. We need to cool off." I grabbed Angel's arm and led her back to the house as the neighbor looked on in disbelief.

No one called the police. I never let anyone if I could prevent it. I even scolded Angel for running to the neighbors.

"Sissy, you don't tell other people what goes on in our house. It is our business." I wrapped my arm around Angel as we sat on her bed and cried.

160

"But dad was hurting you bad." Angel was crying uncontrollably. "I tried to stop him, but he pushed me into the wall."

"I am sorry, honey, he didn't mean to hurt you."

"Mom, she asked, holding me gently. Why don't we leave? Leave for good? I am so tired of the fighting."

"Because I love him. I guess because I love him." I put my face in my hands as Angel squeezed her tiny arms, holding me tighter. "Because I love him." We both continued to cry.

I never went back to my job. I was too embarrassed by Bryan's actions and ashamed of how my face looked, yet I stayed with Bryan. Soon after, we moved again. Without my income from my job, we could no longer afford that nice of a home. Once again, we moved to another town, home, and the children started over in another school system.

We were always running. Running from the shame of our chaotic life, running from bill collectors, and running from our pasts that neither of us ever healed from, dragging Adam and Angel along with us.

Chapter 18
Witness

Adam and Angel witnessed multiple beatings that I took from Bryan. There was nothing they could do but watch and wait for the storm to calm. It always did. After every fight, Bryan and I would make up. Not taking into consideration what the children witnessed, we just continued living.

A new house, a new town, and new friends always seemed like the beginning of a somewhat normal life. Each month I tried to buy Adam and Angel something special with the Social Security money. I wanted them to have things they enjoyed since it seemed they were always leaving stuff behind. It was the only way I knew how to make up for all the chaos we lived in. I was trying to be a good mother amid our crazy lives.

Things would be good for a while, until the next blow up, beating, or move. There was always that calm before the storm. It was almost too good to be true when things were mundane. We all could sense something was coming. It was just a matter of time.

I found another job like I always did, but Bryan, of course, did not work. If he did, it was only for a few weeks. Bryan found excuse after excuse to not hold down a reliable job. If he could not get high, he would quit. If he could not manage to wake up in the mornings, he would get fired. Bryan was not playing music either. In a city as big as Phoenix, there were multiple talented musicians. He was just another one looking for a gig to play.

Chance once told me, "You really scraped the bottom of the barrel when you got with Bryan."

I was starting to believe it and believe that the barrel was running dry. I loved Bryan. More than I had ever loved anyone, but the constant fighting, his inability to provide or be productive made me second guess myself. We had been together ten years now, and nothing had changed. Bryan had not changed, and I was wearing down.

It had been less than a few months since the last severe beating I took from Bryan. I have a long thick scar on the back of my arm as a reminder of that night. I cannot even remember what the fight was about. All I remember was Bryan throwing a potted plant at me. The ceramic pot stayed attached to the plant, and a piece shattered against the wall, cutting my arm with a great deal of force. I did my best to bandage the wound, and I had no plans of getting stitches. I could not afford a hospital visit at the time.

The next morning after the fight, I watched my one-year-old nephew when I had a kitchen fire. Trying to extinguish the fire, I picked up the pan from the stove and threw it outside. The wind caught the flames, blowing them back onto my arms. I suffered severe burns to both of my arms, and I was in a great deal of pain.

Just as I realized what I had done, my nephew began to cry. A knock at the door caught me by surprise but was a relief. The welcome wagon lady was standing there smiling with a basket of samples and coupons as she entered the chaos. Back then, when you moved into a new house, the community sent out a lovely person to welcome you and help you get acquainted with the area. She had no idea what she was walking into.

"Please help me." I stood there in shock as my arms began to blister and blood dripped from my wounded arm from the night before. The young woman picked up my nephew, trying to console him as I made a phone call.

"Matthew, there has been an accident, and I am going to the hospital. The welcome wagon lady is staying with the baby. You need to come now." I said frantically.

"What? I am on my way." Matthew hung up the phone.

Matthew did not know what happened. I had no time to explain. All he knew was that some stranger kept his baby while his sister was transported to the hospital. He left work right away.

The hospital treated my burns, sewed up my arm, and sent me home. No one asked about the wound on my arm because of the severity of the burns. Again, Bryan's abuse went undetected.

Adam and Angel spent many nights with their heads covered with a pillow, trying to drown out the noise of the constant fighting. Scared of what they would wake up to, trying to sleep so they could focus on school, trying not to hear the horrible things being said, and trying not to imagine the worst. So that night was no different. Remembering the horrendous fight from the night before, the children reluctantly opened the door to find me lying on the couch, both arms bandaged and highly medicated, unable to speak clearly.

"Mom, what happened? Mom!" Angel said, trying to get me to respond.

"I am fine," I said, slurring from the pain medication.

164

Angel went into the bathroom, where blood droplets were splattered all over the tile floor, and bloodstained wash clothes laid draped across the sink and bathtub. She began to clean up the blood, scared, and unsure of what happened.

Each beating got worse, each fight escalated quicker, yet I never once called the police. I never let anyone else call either. I always dismissed the beatings, protecting Bryan while I hid bruises, scars, and my brokenness. Bryan had beaten me physically, but I was mentally beaten too.

Bryan made me feel unworthy of love. He made me feel like I was unattractive and useless. He continually reminded me that no one else would have me. Why would they? I was overweight and beaten down by him. I did not have the self-worth to pull myself up out of the hole he dug for me.

It made no sense. On the one hand, Bryan told me everything I was not and how no one would ever want me, but on the other hand, he would confess his undying love for me and how he could not live without me. I did not know what to believe.

Our lives were chaotic, unstable, and unimaginable. Adam and Angel were witnesses to it all.

Chapter 19
The Long-Awaited Break

After a few years of moving from house to house in the Phoenix desert, unable to pay the rent, Bryan finally got the break he had been searching for.

"Babe, guess what? I got the best opportunity. Filled with excitement, Bryan scrambled around looking for decent clothes to wear.

"What! What kind of opportunity?" I said, confused.

"So, remember the guy I told you about that played with Three Dog Night? I ran into him, and he knows a guy that is looking for a lead guitarist for his band."

"Okay, but how is that a great opportunity? It's just a band."

"It's a house band, Babe. It is a permanent gig, every week, steady money. It's on the mountain where all the rich people go to get away from this heat."

"On the mountain? What mountain?"

"The white mountains, Pinetop. It is about 4 hours from here. Only people with money go there to get away, go skiing, and vacation. This band gig is an excellent opportunity."

"So, we would move there?" I was still not understanding as Bryan opened every dresser drawer, throwing clothes around.

"Yes! Do you know how great this could be for me, for us? Now help me find something to wear. I have an audition this weekend, and I can't go dressed like a bum."

Bryan did not have any dress clothes. He never had a use for them. Luckily for him, it was the first of the month, and I just received the children's Social Security check. I took a couple of hundred dollars and bought Bryan some new jeans, dress shirts, and a pair of cowboy boots. I even made sure he had plenty of guitar strings. I was hoping this was the big break, and I wanted to support it. It was not the first time that I spent the Social Security check money on Bryan, though. The children and I might have done without, Bryan did not. Every week he had his bag of pot and cigarettes. Even if the lights got shut off, Bryan had what he wanted. He was more like a child I was raising and less of a husband and father.

Nonetheless, I did what I could to make sure Bryan had what he needed for his audition. Maybe this could be the break he had been waiting for. Maybe, just maybe, he would contribute to our family finally, and I could get a break too.

Bryan's audition was a success. The band loved him and thought he would be a great addition. He could play the guitar just as well as anyone else, and he was versatile in playing rhythm and lead. He was just what they were looking for.

"So, how did it go?" I grabbed Bryan's bag as he made his way through the door.

"It went great. They want me to come up there and be in their band. It is so great up there. You guys will love it." Bryan sat down, lit up a joint, and handed it to me.

"When? When do they want you to start? How much does it pay? Tell me everything." I inhaled.

"They want me to start in two weeks. It pays $400 a week, Rachel.

167

That is more than I have ever made playing music. We will practice every day for a couple of hours, and then we will play Wednesday through Saturday. You don't even have to work. With my check and the Social Security check, we could make it. This is it, Babe. I finally got my break."

We finished the joint as I took it all in. We were moving again to another place and starting all over. I guess my dream of traveling was coming to fruition.

"So, when do we go? What about school for the kids? There is so much to figure out."

"I can go up first, and then you can come up later and try to find us a place. Alan said there are plenty of places to rent because it is a tourist town.

"The kids have a few more weeks before school starts. I should probably start looking soon before it starts back up. Let's go this week. Maybe the kids can stay with the Cole's for a few days."

"That could work. Alan said I could stay with him in the meantime. He is the keyboard player. Rach, you are going to love it up there. It is beautiful."

Bryan and I reluctantly drove our piece of shit car up the mountain, four hours from the heat of Phoenix. Unsure of its ability to make it, the car got us there. We drove through the narrow, winding canyon, stopping on the way to take in the breathtaking views and looking over the edge to see the Colorado River making its path through the rocky canyon side. It was a beautiful sight. Pine trees lined the two-lane highway leading up to the mountain. The crisp air and pine smell was so refreshing coming from the heat of the valley.

It was understandable why people traveled for four hours to this place. It was serene.

 Butted up to the Navajo Indian reservation, there were pine trees as far as the eye could see. The mountain did not have much to offer other than the peace and tranquility that so many people sought. The reason it became a tourist town for those living in and wishing to escape from the hot desert.

 Just an hour north of Pinetop was a small town that became a well-known ski resort. Those who could afford it traveled through Pinetop, a lot of the time staying there for more affordable accommodations. Tourists enjoyed skiing and snowmobiling in the winter months and camping and fishing in the summer.

 In the middle of this small town named Pinetop sat this large two-story bar called Mr. C's. Although the locals enjoyed and frequented the place, it became a regular stopping point for the tourist while staying on the mountain.

 The bar owners were upgrading a few things and were looking to have live music, making it more desirable. They did not want just any band. They wanted a good band that could play a variety of music. They wanted a professional-looking band that would play the type of music appealing to the 40 and over crowd coming from the valley. Those people had money and would spend a lot of it if they were having a good time. Bryan became a part of that band.

Bryan and I were able to secure a place to rent. A hillside cabin at the end of a short road where only two other cabins nestled into the same hill. It was beautiful, fully furnished, and offered an amazing view. Underneath the two-bedroom cabin was a one-bedroom apartment, we let Adam occupy. A teenager who needed his privacy. It was perfect.

A short hike up the cabin's backside, reaching the top of the hill, laid a large rock formation. From that spot, you could see the entire town. It was where Angel spent much of her time escaping the chaos.

Many animals inhabited that mountain. That is probably why Bryan adored it so much, Angel too. They both enjoyed the outdoors and grew close because of their love of nature. Angel was always a daddy's girl and a tomboy. She was close to Chance when he was alive and became close to Bryan, spending a lot of time with him fishing at the local lake. It was called Rainbow lake, a small, beautiful fishing hole surrounded by the mighty pines that scattered that mountain.

Adam didn't care much for the outdoors. He stayed close to me, spending evenings at home, indulging in our favorite snacks, and watching television. We were similar in many ways, I guess. We both found comfort in food, swallowing our feelings bite after bite. A comfort neither of us spoke about.

Bryan settled right into his new life as a band member of the local band. It was only a matter of time before he became well known in the small town, with one grocery store, gas station, and school. It did not take long to become a local.

I was not enjoying the quiet life as much. I missed working, missed having friends, and found myself secluded, especially in the winter months. The children, now teenagers, were making friends and spending more time away from home. Loneliness settled in as I spent most of my time alone.

Bryan discouraged me from going to the bar to watch him play. Unless I was with the other band member's wives, Bryan wanted me to stay home, fearing I would make a scene.

Mr. C's was different than the small honky-tonks he played in back home. Bryan took the job seriously, and he did not want anything to ruin it. He did not want my jealousy to cause a fight, a fight that could escalate and force him to lose his temper. These people saw him as a local star, and if they knew he beat his wife, all that could change for him. The person they thought he was, was not the person he had been for the last ten years or the person he was at home. He needed to protect that image. So, he did, and so did we.

Although Bryan promised me that I could stay home, we found ourselves still struggling. Bryan was spending close to two hundred dollars of his check each week on marijuana, cigarettes, and whatever he needed to maintain his image. Bryan's extra expenditures never left enough money to pay for rent, utilities, and groceries.

I tried to find employment, but the small town offered very few opportunities. I worked in an office part-time, but the little I made did not seem worth it. I managed an Arby's, which I hated. Trying to supplement our income, it seemed I was running into one dead end after another. I was miserable.

Unsatisfied, I began to drink heavily. I passed out every night on the couch after drinking a bottle of rum, trying to pass the time and numb the pain.

Our fighting continued, but I protected him more now than ever. His image had to be maintained, and I was not sure if anyone on that mountain would believe me anyway. They held him in such high regard. All the locals, band members, and wives had such a high image of Bryan that I believed my abuse claims would go unnoticed or dismissed if I did tell anyone.

The children were still aware of the abuse. I guess they had gotten so used to it that it no longer fazed them, but I tried my best to hide it from them anyway. I wanted to save them the embarrassment of anyone knowing what kind of life they lived.

Three years and five moves later, I hated every minute of living on that mountain. Although I never called the police on Bryan in years past, it seemed more of a secret now than ever. I was isolated. I had few friends, a car that barely started or ran, let alone that would make it to the valley. I had no money and an abusive husband that everyone adored. It was the worst situation I could be in.

Chapter 20
The Last Day

We moved once more into a small trailer in a trailer park nestled in the woods. I made the best of it, but I was tired of being isolated, I was tired of Bryan's rumors with other women, and I was tired of being the abused wife that did nothing and said nothing.

Bryan left for work at around 7 pm to play his set every weekend night. The band did not start until 9 pm, but it gave them time to tune everything, mingle with their fans and play one or two songs before starting their set.

This particular night I poured myself a drink and then another, waiting for the right time. I was going to the bar, and Bryan was not going to stop me. I planned to arrive around 11 pm when things would be hopping, and I could quietly slip in the door.

I see a tall blonde with big boobs dancing alone in front of Bryan just as I arrived. Immediately I was furious. All the rumors must be true. It was apparent something was going on with Bryan and this blonde woman. I pulled up a chair and sat down next to one of the other band member's girlfriends. I bought a drink and watched as Bryan and this woman made eye contact with one another. He still had not noticed my arrival. As the woman continued shaking herself in front of Bryan, my friend grabbed my arm and squeezed it. She knew how I must have been feeling; she had felt it before herself.

"Don't do anything stupid, Rachel. It's not worth it." My friend whispered in my ear.

The longer I looked on, the madder I became, trying to resist going over and knocking that woman on her ass. The last song in the set ended. It was now around midnight. The band would play one more set before the night was over. Bryan unhooked his guitar strap and placed his guitar on its stand. He jumped off the stage next to the blonde waiting for him. Smiling and laughing as they walked away. Bryan looked up to see me sitting there, noticeably angry. Bryan motioned for the blonde to go in the opposite direction, not knowing what I might do.

"What are you doing here, Rachel? You know you are not supposed to be here. You just want to start trouble."

"Are you having fun with your little girlfriend? Does she know you are married? Do I need to let her know that her boyfriend has a wife and kids at home? Have you mentioned that to her?"

"Rachel, don't you say a fucking thing to her. She is the owner's sister. Don't you dare embarrass me. Her brother signs my checks, and she is just a fan. Nothing more. You need to leave."

"I am not going anywhere. Sorry to ruin your fun, but that little floozy needs to find someone else's husband to dance in front of and make googly eyes at."

"Rachel, just leave."

"Or what, Bryan? Are you going to show everyone what you are really about? That you are a wife-beater. What are you so afraid of?"

"Leave Rachel or else." Bryan walked back up to the stage.

"Or else what?" I screamed across the room.

Bryan strapped back on his guitar and put his game face on. He stared at me as if threatening me with his eyes. The band began to play, the second song in, here comes the blonde again dancing in front of Bryan. This time he was not as noticeably friendly with her. The song ended, and Bryan leaned down and whispered something to the blonde as I looked on. The blonde exited the dance floor, looked over at me, and smiled.

Halfway through the third song and several drinks later, I got up and made my way to the dance floor. I began dancing in front of Bryan as if to mock the blonde woman.

Bryan mouthed to me, "Leave now. You are fucking embarrassing me."

I was so angry I leaned down and started pulling cords out of amps, slinging them back at Bryan. The other band members were looking at Bryan as if he should be doing something. I continued to grab whatever I could. Bryan took his foot, with the boots I purchased with the children's Social Security money, and kicked me in the forehead. I fell backward as the bouncers made their way to the stage.

"Get her out of here," Bryan said to the bouncers.

The bouncers picked me up by the arms and started walking me to the door. I did not care anymore, continuing to fight them while they drug me through the bar. I was done with Bryan, and with that life, embarrassing him did not mean anything to me anymore.

175

"You mother fuckers don't know who he is. He is nothing but a loser who beats his wife and smokes up all his money. And you, you fucking whore need to stay away from my husband. I will beat your mother fucking ass." I pointed at the blonde as the bouncers continued escorting me out. The band continued to play as everyone looked on in disbelief.

There were a few people who were somewhat aware of the abuse. I had been seen many times around town with black eyes and bruises, but Bryan seemed like such a nice guy that it was hard for them to imagine that he could do such a thing. Bryan dismissed any accusations and told people that I was crazy and how sorry he felt for the kids and me. That is why he stayed. Typical of what most abusers do to put eyes on the other person, but this little outburst made them wonder if it was true. Suppose I was out of my mind. Bryan's manipulation and abuse confused my thoughts so much that, at times, I felt crazy and even acted crazy because of everything Bryan was putting me through. But this time, I had finally lost it. I had enough.

The friend that I sat with earlier took me home. I poured my heart out to her all the way. I did not have many friends. I needed someone to talk to and understand what I was going through.

"He is going to beat my ass when he gets home. I have really done it this time. If I end up dead, he killed me. He is furious." I sobbed.

"Don't say that, Rachel. You need to leave him if he beats you. Why have you stayed all these years?" My friend said, patting me on the leg.

176

"I guess I love him. I don't know. Bryan has been beating on me for the majority of our marriage. Some days are good. I am not perfect, and I know that. I don't know why I stay." I opened the door. "Thanks for the ride."

I braced myself for Bryan's arrival. I knew there was a fight coming. He was not going to let me get away with what I had just done. Shortly after 1:30 am, Bryan came through the door, raging mad. So mad that he didn't stay to mingle after his set was over. He fiercely walked towards me.

"You fucking bitch, you have embarrassed me for the last time."

Bryan punched me as I put my hands up to block the blow. He grabbed me by the shirt and tossed me onto the floor, hitting me in the face and then the chest. I was so drunk I could barely fight back or protect myself as Bryan continued punch after punch.

Awoken by the noise, Adam got out of his bed to see Bryan on top of me, throwing one punch after another.

"Stop it, stop. Get off her." Adam came over to Bryan and put him in a chokehold. The same one, Bryan taught Adam how to do years before. Adam pulled Bryan back and then dropped him. Bryan jumped to his feet.

"Oh, you want some of this too? Come on, big man."

"I don't want to fight you. I want you to quit hitting my mom." Tears welled up in Adam's eyes as he looked at Bryan in disbelief.

Adam standing 6'3 inches, 250lbs, and now an adult, knew he had to do something, but he was tender-hearted. A gentle giant who did not want to hurt anyone, but he was tired too. Tired of standing by and watching this man, the only father he really knew, who supposedly loved his mom, beat on her.

Angel had fallen asleep with a pillow over her head to drown out the noise like she had done many nights before, but the sound of someone crying uncontrollably awoke her. She raised in her bed to see Adam on the floor leaning up against the closed door, sobbing.

"Adam, what happened?" Angel got out of bed and sat next to Adam on the floor.

"Dad wanted to fight me. Can you believe that? He was actually going to fight me." Adam continued to sob.

"It was a big fight, wasn't it?" Angel asked, knowing what she heard. "Where is Mom?"

"I don't know, I guess in the living room. I think dad went to bed."

"Sleep in here tonight if you want. I am going to go check on Mom."

Angel found me sitting on the couch with ice on my face; dried mascara runs down my cheeks from crying. Still dressed in my bar clothes, I looked up at Angel as tears fill my eyes.

"We are leaving. We are leaving today and going back to Indiana. This is over. I can't take this anymore."

"But Mom, what about my friends? I won't get to tell them goodbye." Angel started to cry.

"I am sorry, Sissy, but I have made up my mind. Pack your room. I am going to rent a U-Haul as soon as they open this morning. Try to pack what you can."

I only slept a few hours waiting for the U-Haul company to open. I rented a U-Haul, and the three of us loaded what we could while Bryan laid asleep in the bed. He had no idea we were leaving. Quietly moving things onto the small truck, arranging a mattress to access it through the door from the cab to rest along the way.

I let Adam drive for short periods while I took a break and rested for a few minutes. We all cried on and off during the trip, not knowing that day was one of those last days. I had cried so much I had no tears left to cry.

None of us knew it would be the last day to see our friends, live in that house and on that mountain. We had experienced many last days, but this one was different. It was the last day we would ever see Bryan.

Chapter 21
The Quiet Escape

The children and I, Adam, now 18, and Angel, 16, showed up on my parent's stoop unannounced once again. We had the U-Haul loaded down with what we could manage to get on it the day we left.

No one knew we were coming to Indiana, and no one knew we left Arizona. We just left, no goodbyes and no advance notices, we just disappeared.

My parents were not exactly happy to see the truck pulling into their drive, but they opened their home up to us anyway. They witnessed this before. I would leave, disrupting our lives, only to go back to Bryan after my external and internal wounds healed. After my family helped me pick up the pieces trying to get me back on my feet, I would let him back in. They were fed up too.

"What are you doing here, Rachel?" My mother said as she opened the door.

"We have had enough, Mom. That is the last time that son of bitch is going to put his hands on me."

"Well, I hope you mean it this time. Rachel, you look awful." My mother hugged the children and me. "Let us get you something to eat. Are you hungry?"

"We are starved. Thanks, Mom."

My mother's face had aged a bit since the last time I saw her. Her hair was still black as night, not a single grey hair. I knew she had her own struggles, but I could not recognize anyone else's during mine.

"Hi, Dad! Sorry to barge in like this. We had to leave in a hurry, and I had no time to call." My father sat in his usual spot at the kitchen table. It was past 10 am, which meant he had finished his coffee and starting drinking beer.

"I guess it's alright." My father slurred, obviously drunk he took another drink of his beer, looking down at the newspaper.

"I will find a place to live right away. I can rent a storage unit tomorrow and unload the truck. I did not want to leave everything. We have done that way too many times."

"It's fine. We have space. You and the kids will have to share a room, though." My father said, never looking up from his paper. "You can use that old car out there to look for a job until you can afford to buy one. It isn't much, but if you keep the oil changed, it should last a little while."

"Thanks, Dad. I am sure it will do just fine. We need all the help we can get right now." I got up from the table and headed off to bed.

The next morning we unloaded everything we owned into a small storage unit and took the U-Haul to the local dealer. I left the keys under the mat and left.

The children and I started moving on with our lives. I soon after secured a low-income apartment for Angel and me, while Adam moved to California, where my second baby brother lived. Angel started her junior year in high school in the same school I spent my high school years. This would be the 20th school Angel had attended, but she was adjusting and quickly making friends.

I found a decent paying job, working in an office for a local chemical company.

As I sat in our little apartment, thinking about everything that happened throughout my and Bryan's marriage. All the damage he did to me physically and emotionally. The number of years I wasted trying to make it work with him. My young years. My eyes filled with tears as I thought about what I put my children through.

Then a calm came over me. It was over. I was no longer walking on eggshells in fear of a fight breaking out. I was not worrying if Bryan was sleeping with someone else or trying to force him to work and help support our family. I was finally at peace, I was finally able to smile and feel happy, and I was finally free. I had spent too much time running. I was always running, running from my childhood, Chance, and now Bryan. I was tired of running, never finding peace. It was time to plant my feet and live happily.

I began dating and going out with old friends from my past. I had spent the last 13 years fighting for a marriage that I could not make work. I was done wasting my life.

My father ended up giving me that old car. It was not much. The paint was peeling off, the front seats were broken down, it sucked the gas, and the muffler had come loose, causing a loud noise. I drove it anyway. I was making it work for the time being.

Driving my boyfriend to get cigarettes at the local gas station, I saw red lights in my rearview mirror.

"Oh, shit, I am getting pulled over."
"What did you do?" My boyfriend asked.
"I don't know." I began to panic.

"Ma'am, do you know why I pulled you over?" The officer said as he approached the window. "You have a headlight out. I need to see your license and registration."

"Uh, I don't have them on me. We were just running to the gas station to get cigarettes. I can give you my name and social security number." I said nervously.

"Ma'am, why are you acting so strangely?

"I am just nervous, sir. I don't get pulled over much. My name is Rachel Havens. I just live up the road."

"How about I follow you home, and you can get me those, license. Something is not adding up here. I will be right behind you."

I drove slowly home as I began to cry.

"What is wrong, Rach? You have a license, don't you?"

"I think I have some parking tickets I haven't paid in Arizona. They may have suspended my license. I don't know."

"That isn't that big of a deal. The police will not arrest you or anything. Just explain the situation you left. Surely they will understand."

"I don't think they will understand."

My boyfriend and I strolled up the stairs to my apartment with the police officer close behind us. I opened the door and yelled for Angel.

"Mom, what is going on? Are you in some kind of trouble?"

"I got pulled over, and I left my license here. This officer decided to follow me home so I could give them to him." I pulled out my wallet, and reluctantly gave the officer my license.

"I am going to run these. I will be right back." I sat on the couch, visibly shaking.

"Mom, everything is going to be okay, right?" Angel put her arm around me, waiting for an answer.

"Ma'am, you need to come with me. You are under arrest." The officer grabbed my hands and put me in handcuffs.

"Mom! Mom! Arrest for what, sir?" Angel cried out.

"There is a warrant for your mother's arrest for grand theft auto." The officer started leading me out the door.

"What? She has never stolen a car. This is crazy. Mom! Wait! Can I hug her goodbye?" Angel quickly moved towards the door, putting her arms around me. "I love you, Mom. We will figure this out."

"I love you too, Sissy. I love you too." I hung my head, crying uncontrollably.

I was booked into the county jail, fingerprinted, and issued a jail jumpsuit. I laid on the cold, hard jail bed staring at the ceiling, replaying my whole life in my head, unsure of my future. Crying on and off and dozing in and out. I waited for my initial meeting with my attorney the next morning.

"Good morning, ma'am. My name is Mr. Andrews. I am your court-appointed attorney. I have looked over your file, and you are looking at some pretty serious charges. Do you understand what charges are being brought on you?"

"The arresting officer said that there is a warrant for grand theft auto. That is all I know." I put my head in my hands and then ran my fingers through my hair. I let out a long and loud sigh.

"Yes, that is one of the charges you are facing because you took the U-Haul out of the state when you only paid for a local day rental. Ma'am, you are facing a more serious charge of second-degree murder for the death of your husband."

"Death of my husband? Chance died years ago, and Bryan was very much alive when we left.
I didn't murder anyone." I sat upright in my chair.

"According to witnesses, the two of you fought the night before you left Arizona. Is that true?"

"We fought for 13 years. That night was no different. That does not mean I killed him. Is Bryan dead? No, it can't be," I screamed. "What happened?"

"Rachel, I am here to help you. I am on your side, but if you don't tell me the truth, then I can't help you the best way possible. Your husband was shot and killed the day you left. Do you know anything about that?"

"I am telling you; I didn't kill my husband. I didn't even know he was dead."

"That is why I need you to tell me everything. I can't defend you to the best of my abilities if I don't know what happened." The attorney continued.

"We did have a fight, a big fight. Bryan was punching me when my son came in and stopped it. Bryan went to bed shortly after, and I stayed up until the U-Haul company opened. I rented a U-Haul and told the man that I was just using it around town. I could not afford the $1200 to drive it here, and we needed to leave. We did not have a vehicle that would make it. So, I guess I did steal the truck if that is what they are calling it. But I didn't kill my husband."

"So, you are saying that your husband laid in bed the whole time you and your children moved things onto the truck?"

"Yes. He plays music until the morning hours. He always sleeps till noon or one the next day. He is a hard sleeper. We just thought he was asleep."

"Rachel, they are charging you with his murder. Your story is not going to get you off of these charges. You need to think about every detail so we can plan your defense. I will be back next Thursday. We will talk again then."

The time passed slowly for me in that small jail cell. The women in there were vicious, mostly prostitutes, and drug addicts. I was struggling with what to do and how to do it. I had never been in that position before, and no one could help me this time. Did I want to kill Bryan? Yes, I thought about it many times after he put a beating on me, but I did not kill him. I recalled daydreaming about ways to kill him and get away with it. I loved Bryan. I did not want to kill him; I just wanted him to be everything that he promised me he would be.

Angel was not old enough to visit me in jail, so I called her every chance I got. The only visit I could get with her was looking out the slender jailhouse window to see her standing on the sidewalk below, waving at me. I missed her, and I did not know what would happen to her if they locked me away for good. Where would she go? Who would take care of her? Was she going to have to live in the same house as my father, who destroyed my youth? I was truly broken, and for the first time in my life, I got on my knees and began to pray. I knew that the only person who could help me now was God.

Just like clockwork, my appointed attorney showed up on Thursday to discuss my case further.

"How are you doing, Rachel? Are they treating you okay in here?"

"This place is terrible. I can't take it. The food is horrible, the beds are hard as rocks, and my roommates are having withdrawals and are up all night sick."

"I spoke with the Prosecuting Attorney, and they are willing to cut you a deal."

"Okay. That is good. Right?"

"Well, they want you to confess to the murder of Bryan. They will reduce the charge to manslaughter and drop the grand theft auto charge."

"Confess! But I did not kill him. I swear I did not kill him. I don't know what happened."

"Rachel, if you don't confess, they are going to bring charges on your children for accessory to murder. Your son is an adult, and your daughter could be tried as an adult because of her age. They don't believe you could have killed him alone."

"What? No! My children did not have anything to do with any of this. They cannot do that. My children have been through enough. They have always just been innocent bystanders. How could they make such claims?"

"It is just how the system works, Rachel. They can avoid a costly trial if you confess. If you do not confess, then they will make you wish you did."

"I don't want to confess to a murder I didn't commit. This is so unfair."

"I think you should take the deal, Rachel. I will take your statement and present it to the Prosecuting Attorney. You are looking at 8-10 years in prison."

"8-10 years for something I didn't do? This is insane.

"We can try to get them to take a plea of involuntary manslaughter, claiming the abuse. But, Rachel, I looked, and there has never been one police report filed claiming domestic violence. Not one. Not in any of the states you said you lived in."

I rested my head in my hands.

"I never wanted him to get in trouble. It would have cost money we did not have, and every time he hit me, he told me he would never do it again. I wanted to believe him."

"If you have witnesses, hospital bills, or anything that might show a trail of the abuse, we can present that. Can you think of anything?"

"My children were the only witnesses. I only went to the hospital once, and that was because of burns. They sewed up my arm, but I do not think they documented it. There were always people who saw me after, with black eyes, a broken nose, busted lips, but I usually hid it or dismissed it. I guess I am going to prison."

"We can't use the children as witnesses. Right now, they believe they played some sort of role in Bryan's murder. Without hard proof that you were a victim of domestic violence, they will charge you with second-degree murder if you do not confess. You could be looking at more like 20 years."

"If you take my statement, do you record it?"

"I can if that is how you would like it done."

"If I am going to make a statement, it is going to be the whole story."

"Whatever you want, Rachel. I can come back tomorrow with my recorder, and we can do it then. How does that sound?"

"Okay. I will be waiting for you."

That evening I called my mother and then Angel. I explained to them both that I was going to confess to Bryan's murder and that I would be going to prison.

"Mom, you can't confess to something you didn't do. What am I going to do? Where will I live?"

"I am trying to sort all this out, Sis. They want to bring charges on you and Adam. I am not going to let that happen. I will find someplace for you. The Toney's said you could stay with them and finish school."

"I would have to change schools again."

"I will figure it out. I am confessing tomorrow. Mr. Andrews is taking my statement in the morning. I don't know what will happen after that, but I will call you. I love you."

I could not allow them to bring charges on my children. We all had finally started to get on with our lives and have some sort of normalcy. I could not put them through that even though I knew none of us had anything to do with Bryan's murder. I owed them that much. I had to take the plea or look at spending the rest of my life in prison, or at least the better part of 20 years. I could not fight this without the money for an attorney, so I would confess to something I didn't do.

I laid on that cold hard bed all night thinking about what I wanted to say. I wanted to make a statement that would somehow show what my children and I went through. Maybe, just maybe, the judge would have some sympathy for me. Maybe he would give me a lighter sentence so that someday I could truly move on with my life. I could only hope.

Mr. Andrews showed up the following day to take my statement just like he said he would. Carrying in this 1980's cassette recorder, Mr. Andrews flung it onto the stainless-steel table in the visiting room. He looked like he had a rough night with his hair windblown and a five o'clock shadow.

"Rachel, when you are ready, I will start the recorder. Let's get you something to drink. If you need to stop, just raise your hand, and we can take a break. Are you ready?" Mr. Andrews pushed the recorder in front of me.
"I am ready." I leaned back in the hard metal chair and took a deep breath.

Mr. Andrews pressed the record button and nodded at me to begin. I starred at the green light on the recorder as I began to speak.

"Bryan and I started to see each other before I divorced my first husband. I fell deeply in love with him. He was everything I could ever imagine. He was kind, affectionate, and man; the sex was amazing. He really took to my children, and that was important to me too.
We fought many times, but the fights did not get too physical until after the accident in Kansas, where he killed his friend. He was protecting us and was never charged with anything. He did what he had to do, and I never blamed him for that, but he could not forgive himself.
After that, every fight led to a physical confrontation. At first, it was just one hit, but over time it was repeated hits. He broke my nose several times, blacked my eyes, and busted my lips.

190

He choked me, punched my chest, kicked me, and swung me by the arms. Anything you can think of.

After every fight, he would apologize, and we would make up. I felt sorry for him after what he went through. Hank was his friend, our friend, and I knew that it did something to him. It changed him; he was never the same. I just wanted him to get past it, move on and start living again, but he never could. It was like the accident stirred up the violence in him.

We were always moving because we could not pay our bills. Bryan never wanted to work, and it was a struggle for me to try to pay for everything. We fought a lot about that.

I wanted to believe he did not want to hurt me. I sometimes thought it was my fault. Maybe I should have kept my mouth shut; maybe I should have walked away, and maybe I should have left him for good. I never wanted to see him go to jail, though. We could not afford it. I guess a part of me always knew I would take him back. I anticipated the making up, and I did not want to cause us future financial trouble by calling the police every time we had a confrontation.

I knew he had a good side to him, and we did have some good times though they were few. After every fight, there was something that ignited in us both. I can't even explain it, but it was almost like things were the way they were when we first started dating. The feelings, passion, and desire for each other was so strong. It was like we were chasing a drug, trying to get that high feeling, repeating the cycle over and over again. It was like he had to hit me and explode for us to get back to that feeling. We chased it for 13 years.

My kids watched it all. As they got older, I tried to keep it from them, but they still knew. They saw the black eyes and bruises; they heard the fighting while lying in their beds at night. I cannot believe I put them through all of it.

When Bryan finally got his break, and we moved to the mountain, we had been suffering for years because of him. Those people thought he was so great. They thought Bryan was this wonderful man, husband, and father. He really was not. They did not know what the kids and I had been through with him. They did not know about the abuse or all the struggles. He was trying to put on this image of a person that, deep down, wasn't him.

I resented it.
I resented him.

For three years, we lived on that mountain under this façade. The abuse did not stop. It was just more important to keep it a secret because Bryan was getting a paycheck for once in our marriage. He did not want that messed up. He believed he was a local star, and we were expected to protect that image that everyone had of him at all cost. I had enough. I had enough of the abuse, enough of the cheating, and enough of the constant struggles.

I started the fight that night. I know I should not have pulled out his guitar chords, but he was adamant about me not going to the bar for months. I knew something was going on. It was not the first time.

I braced myself when I got home. I knew he was going to be furious and that he was going to hit me. He was, and he did. My son pulled him off me. Tears filled his eyes when Bryan tried to fight him. My baby boy was heartbroken; it was not right.

  Before Bryan got home that night, I took the 9mm handgun from the side table and put it under the couch. I feared he would kill me this time. After Adam went to his room, Bryan went to bed. I kind of think Bryan might have been a little scared of what Adam could do to him. He is a big boy and could have hurt Bryan if he wanted to, but he loved him. He did not want to hurt him. Adam just wanted Bryan to stop hitting me.

I snapped.

  You can do whatever you want to me, but you are not going to hurt my children. They were just innocent bystanders who did not ask for this life. So, I grabbed the gun from under the couch and waited until I could hear Bryan snoring. I went into the bedroom, turned on the radio, put two pillows by his head, pointed the gun into the pillow, and pulled the trigger. I walked out and closed the door. Soon after, Angel came out from her room, and I told her we were leaving and that she needed to start packing. We left that day and never looked back."

Mr. Andrews sat quietly listening as I cried, smiled, and then cried again.

  "Rachel, are you sorry for what happened?" He asked.

"Sorry? I am sorry. Sorry that I spent 13 years of my life, my young years, in that marriage. I am sorry that my children had to endure all that they have. I am sorry that my family was continually picking up the pieces, trying to help me put my life back together. I am sorry that I did not think enough of myself to leave years ago. I am sorry for all that I missed through the years, consumed with a chaotic marriage. I am not sorry that I killed Bryan, and I would do it all over again. It was the only way I was able to escape the hold he had on me for so long. The only way we could quietly escape."

Mr. Andrews stopped the recorder and looked down at his file folder. I think something I said must have struck a chord with him. A look of pity came over his face. I believe he understood why I was doing what I was doing.

"Mr. Andrews, I didn't kill my husband, but if you need a confession so I can protect my children, there is your confession."
"Rachel, I don't believe you killed your husband. I am sorry that this is how the justice system works. In my experience, sometimes it is an unjust justice system. I am sorry for that."

Coming Soon!

The Quiet Escape
The Unjust Justice System

Cycle of Abuse

  Years of research have shown that abuse has a pattern, and the abusers have a pattern. So why then can't we spot the abuser? Why can't we find a way to change this cycle that has gone on for years and years? Why do we find ourselves or our loved ones amid the pattern of abuse? It is simple. We don't educate our children to spot the abuse. We don't teach them to tell someone if they have been sexually, physically, and/or emotionally abused or if they are witnesses to such abuse. Our education system is not designed to teach these things, and the abuse is generally coming from their own homes. The place where they should be taught is where many children's innocence is being taken away at the hands of an adult that they look to for love, affection, and security.
  Just like many others, I found myself telling adults in my life about the abuse that went on in our home. Only to be scolded for speaking out. See, my mother, the victim, saw the good in her abuser, and by the time I was speaking out, the incident was over, and they were back in the honeymoon stage. She didn't want that stage to be interrupted by something that was already done. It seemed as if I was wrong to tell anyone about what was going on in our home. I risked being in trouble because those secrets didn't leave our family. It happened; you forgot about it and moved on. I am not sure anyone knew besides us, and if they did, they weren't doing anything about it. Why? Because they couldn't.

The Predator

  A victim will protect their abuser, sometimes at all cost.
They will hide black eyes behind sunglasses, make up
stories about how they fell down the stairs, or say
anything to keep the abuser from having to face the
consequences of their actions. It sounds ridiculous, but at
the point, the abuse begins, the abuser has convinced
their victim that it is partially their fault or all their fault.
The abuser has diminished any self-confidence that the
victim may have or had. The abuser will convince their
victim that anyone standing up against their relationship
is a trouble maker and doesn't want to see them happy.
The victim becomes convinced that the only true
happiness that can be found is with their abuser.
  These things don't happen overnight, but it doesn't take
long for an abuser to control their victim. Why? Because
they are predators who seek out those they know they
can control and manipulate. Most predators themselves
were once victims or witnessed similar abuse. The same
abuse they are using to control their victims is the same
or similar to the abuse they once experienced. It is a
taught behavior, usually taught in their own home as
they were growing up. Unless they recognize the signs
and decide to change the pattern, they will likely become
a predator or a victim.
  I believe some abusers prey on their victims. They seek
out a particular type of person that they feel they can
take control over. What does that person look like?

A likely victim may have some or all of these signs.

1.   Low self-esteem
2.   A strong desire to find companionship

3.   Broken family relationships
4.   Childhood abuse
5.   Family dysfunction
6.   Few or no close friends
7.   Eating disorders
8.   Psychological issues

The honeymoon stage

  An abuser will find a person who is broken in some aspect of their life. The abuser will become the victim's confidant and companion. They will show them affection, sympathy, and love. The abuser will pour on the charm, showering their victim with gifts, flowers, sweet gestures, and expressing their undying love for them. An abuser may convince their victim that they will have a family, unlike the one they did or didn't have. If they have children, the abuser may go above and beyond with the child or children.

  This stage is called the Honeymoon stage. It is this stage where every victim gets roped into the cycle of abuse. It is this stage that the victim keeps hoping to get back to. It is at this stage that the victim unknowingly begins to cover for their abuser. The victim becomes convinced that the abuser has a good side and a softer side. It is this side that caused them to fall in love with their abuser, to begin with. Most victims don't even recognize the abuse when it begins to happen. They don't know they are being abused because their abuser has so manipulated them that their minds can't clearly tell them otherwise. Psychological and emotional manipulation is how abusers control their victims.

The abuse

When an abuser becomes confident that they have their victim in their grasp, they strike. Most victims of abuse were married to their abusers less than six months into their relationship. A quick marriage or the birth of a child makes the abuser feel in control. The abuser uses the union and the children as a bargaining tool to get their victim to stay or make them feel guilty for trying to leave. It's a way to control them.

The abuser doesn't strike right away. Striking quickly would be too obvious, and ironically they lack the confidence in themselves to believe they can keep the victim because they also suffer from low self-esteem. The abuser's lack of confidence makes the abuse happen gradually. Harsh words or outburst of anger begin the cycle. An occasional throwing of an object across the room to insert their control or checking up on their victim to confirm they are where they say they are. Each small incident that is overlooked or brushed off confirms to the abuser that they have control over the situation.

Once they feel they have control is when the incidents will start. An abuser may start by yelling verbal slurs at their victim, blaming the victim for their shortcomings, calling their victim terrible names, or accusing them of infidelity. Emotional abuse is so hard to detect or recognize because the abuser will brush it off, saying they were playing around and how the victim is uptight and can't take a joke. But it is the emotional abuse that leads to physical abuse. The breakdown of someone's sense of self-worth is what allows them to be victimized.

Then the physical abuse can take place once the emotional abuse has set in. A playful smack or push is a sign of the abuser testing their boundaries. Threats of violence, intimidation, smacking, punching, and biting are all abuse.

Statistics show that abused victims will leave their abusers seven times before they leave for good. So, the victim may leave, but they will likely return.

The return

Victims will return to their abusers because the abuser will turn back on the charm in fear of losing control. The abuser will be apologetic, remorseful, or make excuses for the abuse. They will deny the abuse or minimize it, making the victim question their own thoughts about the incident.

The abuser will make promises, not only about not letting it happen again but about other things that might have led up to the incident. If the abuser is unemployed, they will promise to get a job. If the abuser drinks or does drugs, they will promise to stop. If the abuser isn't paying enough attention to the victim, they will promise nights of romance. If the abuser has been unfaithful, they will promise to stay faithful.

Once the victim returns, the honeymoon stage begins again. The stage that started it all, so the cycle repeatedly repeats until, hopefully, the victim leaves for good.

If you are in crisis, contact The National Domestic Violence Hotline at 1-800-799-SAFE (7233) or www.TheHotline.org.

This book is dedicated to my mother and anyone who has endured sexual, mental, and physical abuse from someone they love or loved. May you know that it is not your fault, you deserve to be loved, you are worth more, you are strong, and together we can help others from becoming a victim.

Special thanks to my dear friend and mentor Carla Griffin and my friend Brandy Pardo.

To the brave women who have shared their personal stories with me, you are no longer a victim but a victor.

Lastly, to my husband, who will never read this book, but listened to me for hours during my journey. Who didn't understand the process but gave me space and time to write. I am so happy to share this wonderful life with you.

I love you all.

About the Author

Angela lives in Indiana with her husband, with who she co-owns a small trucking company. She also works at a local university where she is involved in mentoring young adults and actively participates in programs to bring sexual assault and domestic violence awareness on campus. She is a certified Green Dot instructor for the institution. The Green Dot training program teaches sexual assault, domestic violence, and stalking prevention. Angela has been a writer most of her life, although she has only recently begun to publish her work. Angela is the proud parent of two grown children and grandmother to two adored granddaughters.

Photo courtesy of: Free your soul photography

CPSIA information can be obtained
at www.ICGtesting.com
Printed in the USA
LVHW051609280221
680194LV00011B/926